ADDISON WESLEY

Math
Makes Sense

Author Team

Michelle Jackson	Sharon Jeroski
Carole Saundry	Cathy Anderson
Maureen Dockendorf	Brenda Lightburn
Maggie Martin Connell	Michelle Skene
Heather Spencer	Donna Beaumont
Lynn Bryan	Jennifer Travis

PEARSON

Addison
Wesley

Publishing Team

Claire Burnett
Lynn Pereira
Rosalyn Steiner
Ellen Davidson
Keltie Thomas
Susan Ginsberg
Lynne Gulliver
Elynor Kagan
Stephanie Cox
Denise Wake
Judy Wilson

Publisher

Susan Green

Product Manager

Anne-Marie Scullion

Photo Research

Karen Hunter

Design

Word & Image Design Studio Inc.

ISBN 0-321-11536-8

Printed and bound in Canada

3 4 5 TCP 07 06 05

The information and activities presented in this book have been carefully edited and reviewed. However, the publisher shall not be liable for any damages resulting, in whole or in part, from the reader's use of this material.

The publisher has taken every care to meet or exceed industry specifications for the manufacturing of textbooks.

Brand names that appear in this book are intended to provide children with a sense of the real-world applications of mathematics and are in no way intended to endorse specific products.

Acknowledgments

The publisher wishes to thank the following sources for photographs, illustrations, and other materials used in this text. Care has been taken to determine and locate ownership of copyright material in this book. We will gladly receive information enabling us to rectify any errors or omissions in credits.

Cover

Cover illustration by Marisol Sarrazin © 2001. Taken from *Nose to Toes* by Marilyn Baillie with permission of Maple Tree Press Inc.

Illustrations

Hélène Desputeaux, pp. 63–74, 165–176, 267–280; Virginie Faucher, pp. 119–138, 201–221; Tina Holdcroft, pp. 251–266; Linda Hendry, pp. 17–42, 76, 181–200; Vesna Krstanovich, pp. 1–16, 43–62, 101–118, 139–180; Albert Molnar, pp. 79–100; Michel Rabagliati, pp. 282, 284; Anne Villeneuve, pp. 223–250

Photography

Gilbert Duclos, pp. 75 (girl with helmet), 177 (boy holding onto bar), 281 (girl planting seeds); Ray Boudreau, pp. 75–78; Ian Crysler, pp. 177–180, 281–284; Jane Burton/Dorling Kindersley Media Library, p. 77 (dog); Kitchin/Hurst/firstlight.ca, p. 77 (spider); Comstock Images, p. 177 (stoplight)

Contents

Program Consultants and Advisers

Program Consultants

Craig Featherstone
Maggie Martin Connell
Trevor Brown

Assessment Consultant
Sharon Jeroski

Primary Mathematics and Literacy Consultant
Pat Dickinson

Elementary Mathematics Adviser
John A. Van de Walle

British Columbia Early Numeracy Project Adviser
Carole Saundry

Ontario Early Math Strategy Adviser
Ruth Dawson

Program Advisers

Pearson Education thanks its Program Advisers, who helped shape the vision for *Addison Wesley Mathematics Makes Sense* through discussions and reviews of prototype materials and manuscript.

Anthony Azzopardi	Linden Gray	Lois Marchand
Sandra Ball	Pamela Hagen	Cathy Molinski
Bob Belcher	Dennis Hamaguchi	Bill Nimigon
Judy Blake	Angie Harding	Eileen Phillips
Steve Cairns	Peggy Hill	Evelyn Sawicki
Daryl Chichak	Auriana Kowalchuk	Shannon Sharp
Lynda Colgan	Gordon Li	Martha Stewart
Marg Craig	Werner Liedtke	Lynn Strangway
Jennifer Gardner	Jodi Mackie	Mignonne Wood
Florence Glanfield	Kristi Manuel	

Sorting and Patterning

 FOCUS

Children talk about the sorted objects in the picture.

 HOME CONNECTION

Ask your child to describe the picture and explain why the sorted objects are together.

Name: _____   Date: _____

Dear Family,

Your child is starting the first unit in mathematics and will be learning about sorting and patterning.

The Learning Goals for this unit are to

- Recognize attributes. Children look for things they think have something in common. For example, they may choose objects that are the same colour, size, or shape.
- Describe and draw patterns.
- Talk about a pattern rule.
- Use one attribute to make a pattern.

You can help your child reach these goals by doing the activities suggested at the bottom of each page.

Name: _____ Date: _____

Sorting Every Day

Show one way to sort objects at school.

 FOCUS

Children cut and paste from *Line Master 3: Sorting at School* to sort objects found in the classroom.

HOME CONNECTION

Sort laundry or grocery items into groups with your child (for example, all socks, all shirts). Talk about how the items in each group are the same.

Name: _____ Date: _____

Same and Different

Show one way to sort the animals.

What other ways can you sort the animals?

FOCUS

Children cut, paste, and sort farm animals by different attributes (number of feet, size, fur/feathers), using *Line Master 4: Same and Different*.

HOME CONNECTION

Collect various shoes at home and put them in a pile. Ask your child to sort them (summer/winter; laces/Velcro; adult/child). Ask: "How did you decide what to put in each pile?"

Name: _____ Date: _____

Heads Up!

How are the pictures the same?
How are they different?
Circle groups that are the same.

What other ways can you sort the pictures?

Name: _____   Date: _____

Which One Does Not Belong?

Circle the one that does not belong.

 FOCUS

Children choose an item that doesn't belong according to attributes they identify. There are multiple correct answers.

 HOME CONNECTION

Ask your child to explain why some objects don't belong. For example, "Why did you circle the cat?" (Cat is real; other animals are toys.)

6   **Unit I, Lesson 2:** Identify Attributes

Name: _____ Date: _____

My Pattern

Draw a picture of your pattern.

Name: _____   Date: _____

Copy a Pattern

Use cubes to make a pattern.
Copy the pattern.

Make another pattern.
Copy the pattern.

Choose a friend's pattern.
Copy the pattern.

 FOCUS

Children use Snap Cubes or blocks to make a
pattern. Then they copy the pattern by colouring the
blocks on the page.

 HOME CONNECTION

Go on a pattern hunt at home with your child. See
how many things you can find that have patterns
(sweaters, socks, rugs, dishes). Ask your child to
describe the patterns.

Colour Patterns

Colour to show a pattern.

 FOCUS

Children identify the colour pattern and complete the pattern shown.

 HOME CONNECTION

Make a colour pattern using different colour crayons or markers, such as green, green, yellow; green, green, yellow; green, green, yellow. Have your child describe the pattern and tell what comes next.

Unit I, Lesson 3: Recognize and Copy a Pattern

9

Make a Pattern

Use these pictures.
Make two different patterns.

 FOCUS

Children make two different patterns, cutting and pasting images from *Line Master 8: Make a Pattern.*

 HOME CONNECTION

With your child, cut out pictures from newspaper flyers or magazines to make a pattern (vegetable, vegetable, fruit).

Name: _____   Date: _____

What Comes Next?

Draw what comes next in the pattern.

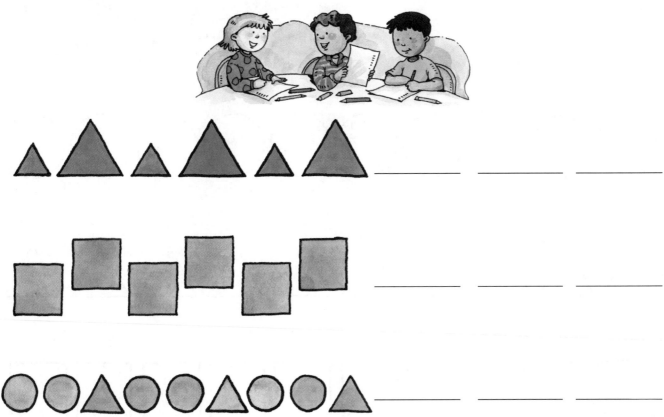

Make a pattern. Ask a friend to draw what comes next.

 FOCUS

Children name and extend a pattern.

 HOME CONNECTION

With your child, use common items like plastic juice-bottle caps or stickers to begin a pattern. Then, ask your child, "What comes next in the pattern?" Complete the pattern together.

Pattern Practice

Make a colour pattern.

 FOCUS

Children make and extend a pattern.

 HOME CONNECTION

Use household objects to practise making many different kinds of patterns (spoon, spoon, fork; spoon, spoon, fork; spoon, spoon, fork).

Find the Pattern

Some beads fell off a necklace. What colour are they?
Colour the missing beads.

 FOCUS

Children identify the pattern and colour the missing beads.

 HOME CONNECTION

With your child, begin a pattern such as mug, mug, glass; mug, mug, glass. Ask your child to complete the pattern.

On Parade

Find the pattern. Show who is missing.

 FOCUS

Children cut and paste from *Line Master 9: On Parade* to identify the missing parts of each pattern.

 HOME CONNECTION

With your child, make a pattern with pens, pencils, crayons, or markers. Repeat the pattern three times. Remove two objects. Ask your child: "What is missing? How do you know?"

My Pattern Border

Draw the pattern for your border.

 FOCUS

Children draw the patterns they will use
for the unit assessment task.

 HOME CONNECTION

Tell your child: "Describe the pattern you used on
your pattern border."

Name: _____ Date: _____

My Journal

Tell what you learned about sorting and patterning.
Use pictures, numbers, or words.

 FOCUS

Children reflect on and record what they learned
about sorting and patterning in this unit.

HOME CONNECTION

Ask your child: "What pattern could you make
using your favourite people, foods, or books?"

Number Relationships

FOCUS

Children talk about the picture and identify the numbers of objects.

HOME CONNECTION

Together, look at the picture and ask: "Where is there a group of four? a group of six? How do you know?" Have your child point to each object while counting aloud.

Name: _____ Date: _____

Dear Family,

This unit will focus on deepening your child's understanding of number relationships.

The Learning Goals for this unit are to

- Read and print numerals to 20.
- Read and print number words to ten.
- Count from 0 to 20. Count backwards from 10 to 0.
- Use a calculator to count to 20.
- Count by matching the number word to the objects being counted.
- "Build" numbers by arranging and rearranging objects.
- Compare and order numbers and groups of objects using words such as *more, less,* and *same.*
- Estimate the number of objects and check by counting.
- Use real-life materials to help solve simple number problems.

You can help your child reach these goals by doing the activities suggested at the bottom of each page.

Count the Fish

Count the fish in each group.
Print the numerals.

_____

_____

_____

_____

 FOCUS

Children count the number of fish in each group and record the numerals.

 HOME CONNECTION

Using small objects, ask your child to show you groups from 1 to 10.

Unit 2, Launch: Number Relationships   **19**

Name: _____ Date: _____

At the Pond

How many do you see?
Print the numerals and number words.

2 ___ two ___

___ ___

___ ___

___ ___

___ ___

FOCUS
Children count the number of creatures and objects in the picture and record the corresponding numerals and number words for 1 to 5.

HOME CONNECTION
Together, collect several sets of four small objects (for example, four buttons, four keys, four pencils). Ask your child to count the number in each set. Ask: "How are these sets alike?" (All have four.)

Name: _____ Date: _____

Count the Birds

Count the number in each group.
Print the numerals and number words.

_____ _____

_____ _____

_____ _____

_____ _____

_____ _____

 FOCUS

Children count the number in each group and record
the corresponding numerals and number words for 6
to 10.

 HOME CONNECTION

With your child, collect sets of one to ten objects (for
example, six stuffed animals, nine envelopes, two
towels). Have your child count the objects. Ask:
"Which set has the most? Which has the least?"

Name: _____ Date: _____

My Calculator

Fill in the white keys on the calculator.

I can use my calculator to _____

_____

_____.

 FOCUS
Children fill in the keys with the appropriate numerals.

 HOME CONNECTION
Discuss why people use calculators. If you have a calculator at home, ask your child to press the clear key to begin and then press whatever number you call out from 1 to 9.

22 **Unit 2, Lesson 2:** Using a Calculator   Copyright © 2004 PEARSON Education Canada Inc. Not to be copied.

Number Search

How many are in the fridge?
Print the numerals and number words.

             _____   _____

          _____   _____

          _____   _____

          _____   _____

          _____   _____

          _____   _____

 FOCUS

Children count items and record numerals and
number words for groups of objects.

HOME CONNECTION

Play "I Spy," giving the number as a clue: "I spy,
with my little eye, something that has four legs."
Your child might guess "table" or "chair." Switch
roles.

Unit 2, Lesson 3: Number Search **23**

Name: _____ Date: _____

Number Pictures

Draw a picture to match each numeral.
Print the number words.

q _____ nine _____

5 _____

7 _____

My number

___ _____

Name: _____ Date: _____

I Can Build Numbers

Choose two numbers.
Show the numbers two ways.

My number _____

One way	Another way

My number _____

One way	Another way

 FOCUS
Children represent numbers in different ways.

 HOME CONNECTION
Have your child explain how the drawings for each number are alike and how they are different.

Name: _____ Date: _____

Pictures of 6

Use counters to show 6.

Draw pictures of ways you can show 6.

FOCUS

Children show the number 6 in a variety of ways.

HOME CONNECTION

Use buttons, keys, or other small objects and ask your child to show the number 4 in different ways.

Name: _____ Date: _____

Ways to Show 7

Colour the cubes to show ways to make 7.
Write how many of each colour.

_____ red _____ blue

_____ red _____ blue

_____ red _____ blue

_____ red _____ blue

 FOCUS

Children use red and blue Snap Cubes to build
different arrangements of 7. To show their
arrangements, they shade in the number of each
colour and write the numerals below.

 HOME CONNECTION

Together, collect 7 objects. Ask your child to count
them. Rearrange the objects in the set and ask,
"How many are there now?" (There are still 7 even
though the arrangement is different.)

Unit 2, Lesson 4: Number Arrangements **27**

More or Less

Draw counters to show more or less.

(counters)	Show 2 more.
(counters)	Show I more.
(counters)	Show I less.
(counters)	Show 2 less.
(counters)	Show I more.
(counters)	Show 2 more.

 FOCUS

Children represent numbers by drawing counters that show one more, one less, two more, two less.

HOME CONNECTION

Ask your child to describe and explain the number of counters your child drew.

Name: _____ Date: _____

Number Challenge

Print the numerals and number words.
Here are your clues.

I more than 8   9   nine

2 more than 5   _____   _____

I less than 3   _____   _____

2 less than 6   _____   _____

I more than 4   _____   _____

2 less than 5   _____   _____

2 more than 4   _____   _____

 FOCUS
Using the clues on this page, children work with a
partner. They record their answers by showing both
the numeral and the number word for each clue.

HOME CONNECTION
Use small objects and ask your child to show a number such as 5. Then have your child show I more and
2 less.

Unit 2, Lesson 5: One and Two More, One and Two Less **29**

Name: _____ Date: _____

Fantastic Five!

Count the number of counters.
Record the numerals.

_____ is _____ more than 5.

_____ is _____ less than 5.

_____ is _____ less than 5.

_____ is _____ more than 5.

(My numbers) Draw counters. Record the numerals.

_____ is _____ more than 5.   _____ is _____ less than 5.

 FOCUS
Children use five-frames to compare numbers to 5.

 HOME CONNECTION
Draw a five-frame (see above) on a piece of paper;
use pennies or buttons as counters. Ask your child to
show you how to make numbers from 0 to 10 using
the five-frame.

Terrific Ten!

Count the number of counters.
Record the numerals.

_____ is _____ less than 10.   _____ is _____ less than 10.

_____ is _____ less than 10.   _____ is _____ less than 10.

 Draw counters. Record the numerals.

_____ is _____ less than 10.   _____ is _____ less than 10.

 FOCUS
Children use ten-frames to compare numbers to 10.

 HOME CONNECTION
Make a ten-frame on paper or by cutting two sections off an egg carton. Ask your child to show a number on this page by placing objects in the ten-frame.

Unit 2, Lesson 7: Terrific Ten **31**

Name: _____   Date: _____

Ten-Frame Numbers

Draw counters to show how many.

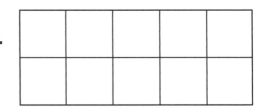

FOCUS

Children draw counters on ten-frames to represent numbers up to 10.

HOME CONNECTION

Make a ten-frame on paper or by cutting two sections off an egg carton. Suggest a number and have your child use objects to show you the number on the ten-frame.

Name: _____   Date: _____

I Can Make 16!

Draw 10 counters on one side.
Draw counters on the other side to make 16.

16 is 10 and _____.

 FOCUS

Children draw or trace counters to show 16 as
"10 and ..." (6).

 HOME CONNECTION

Your child is using "10 and ..." to represent numbers
from 11 to 20. Count out 14 small objects. Ask your
child to put 10 to one side; then count the remaining
counters: "14 is 10 and 4."

Unit 2, Lesson 8: Represent Numbers 10 to 20

Numbers to 20

Print the numerals to show 10 and more.

_____ is 10 and _____.

_____ is 10 and _____.

_____ is 10 and _____.

_____ is 10 and _____.

_____ is 10 and _____.

_____ is 10 and _____.

_____ is 10 and _____.

FOCUS

Using ten-frames, children identify and record numbers to 20.

HOME CONNECTION

Using ten-frames (similar to the ten-frames on this page), ask your child to show each number from 11 to 20.

34   Unit 2, Lesson 8: Represent Numbers 10 to 20

Show Numbers to 20

Choose two numbers between 10 and 20.
Draw counters to show numbers on the two-part mat.

My number _____

My number _____

FOCUS

Children identify, record, and represent numbers to 20 on a two-part mat.

HOME CONNECTION

Gather 20 counters (such as bread tags or buttons). Show your child a group of 10 counters and up to 8 more. Ask: "How many? What is two more? What is two less?"

Name: _____ Date: _____

About How Many?

Estimate the number of cubes.
Spill and count the cubes.

Cubes	Estimate	Count
(dark cube)	about	
(white cube)	about	
(white and dark cubes)	about	

There are _____ and _____ .

There are _____ cubes in all.

FOCUS
Children estimate the number of red and white cubes in a bag; then they count to check their estimates, recording the results.

HOME CONNECTION
Practise estimating with 12 to 18 small, scattered objects. Ask: "Is the number of objects closer to 5 or 10? About how many are there?" Count to check. Repeat with a different number of objects.

Name: _____ Date: _____

I Can Estimate!

Take a handful.
Estimate the number.
Spill the objects.
Count them.

My estimate is _____ .

I counted _____ .

My estimate is _____ .

I counted _____ .

My estimate is _____ .

I counted _____ .

My estimate is _____ .

I counted _____ .

 FOCUS

Children take a handful of each object. They
estimate, count, and record how many in a handful.
Then they repeat the activity.

 HOME CONNECTION

Place 10 to 20 small objects, such as marbles, into a
cup. Have your child estimate the number of objects
in the cup; then count them together. Repeat the
activity with a variety of objects and containers.

Unit 2, Lesson 9: Estimate Numbers

Name: _____ Date: _____

How Many Apples?

There are 8 apples in a bag.
Some are yellow. Some are red.
How many of each could there be?

Show your thinking in pictures, numbers, or words.

 FOCUS

Children figure out possible combinations of eight
red and yellow apples. They express their solutions
using pictures, numbers, or words.

 HOME CONNECTION

When problem solving, your child may discover
more than one correct answer. Ask your child to
explain how he or she solved this problem.

38 Unit 2, Lesson 10: Strategies Tool Kit

Copyright © 2004 Pearson Education Canada Inc. Not to be copied.

Name: _____ Date: _____

What Is in the Backpack?

There are 7 things in the backpack.
Some are books. Some are snacks.

How many could be books? _____

How many could be snacks? _____

Show your thinking in pictures, numbers, or words.

 FOCUS
Children figure out possible combinations of 7 books
and snacks. They express their solutions using
pictures, numbers, or words.

 HOME CONNECTION
Give your child sets of nickels and pennies. Ask:
"How can you use these objects to find an answer to
the backpack problem?" There are many answers.

Name: _____   Date: _____

Show What You Know about 12

Build 12 in two ways.
Use pictures, numbers, or words.

12 twelve

12 twelve

What other ways can you show 12?

 FOCUS
Children use objects to build 12 in different ways.
They record their thinking, using pictures, numbers,
or words.

 HOME CONNECTION
This activity gives your child a chance to show what
he or she has learned about numbers. Ask: "How
did you know so many different ways to build 12? Tell
me about your thinking."

12! 12! 12!

Show 12 objects in two or three groups.
Use pictures, numbers, or words.

Tell a story about what you showed.

 FOCUS

Children build 12 from two or three groups. Then
they tell a story about their number groupings.

 HOME CONNECTION

Your child has been using objects to learn about
numbers 10 to 20. Provide a set of 16 to 20 objects,
such as coins or blocks. Invite your child to count
aloud (or count aloud together).

My Journal

Tell what you learned about numbers.
Use pictures, numbers, or words.

 FOCUS

Children reflect on and record what they learned about number relationships.

HOME CONNECTION

Invite your child to share thoughts about working with numbers in this unit. Also ask: "What have you learned? What do you want to practise?"

Time, Temperature, and Money

 FOCUS

Children talk about the winter scene and discuss when the activities are occurring, focusing on the season and time of day.

 HOME CONNECTION

Ask your child to describe the illustration. Talk about how each season affects our activities.

Dear Family,

In this unit, your child will be learning about time, temperature, and money.

The Learning Goals for this unit are to

- Understand temperature as it relates to seasons and activities.
- Describe and order events, that happen in a day.
- Identify key events, such as birthdays.
- Compare the duration of events, such as recess and lunchtime.
- Name the seasons and days of the week.
- Tell time to the hour.
- Make groups of coins up to 10 cents.

You can help your child reach these goals by doing the activities suggested at the bottom of each page.

Name: _____   Date: _____

Summer Days

Draw a picture about summer.

[picture box]

In the summer, I _____

_____

_____.

Name: _____ Date: _____

Buddy Gets a Bath

Cut and paste the pictures in order.

1		**2**	

3		**4**	

 FOCUS

To sequence the events related to bathing Buddy the dog, children cut and paste pictures from *Line Master 3: Buddy Gets a Bath.*

HOME CONNECTION

Look through family photos with your child and talk about special moments (for example, first steps, first words, birthdays, vacations). Work together to place the pictures in order.

Name: _____ Date: _____

I Can Show the Seasons!

Show the seasons where you live.

spring | summer

winter | fall

FOCUS

Children represent each season by drawing pictures.

HOME CONNECTION

With your child, talk about how temperature varies from season to season. Discuss how clothing and activities change according to the season.

What Is the Order?

| first | second | third | fourth | fifth | sixth | seventh | eighth | ninth | tenth |
| 1st | 2nd | 3rd | 4th | 5th | 6th | 7th | 8th | 9th | 10th |

Colour the cars.

third ▐green▷ sixth ▐red▷ second ▐yellow▷ tenth ▐blue▷ fourth ▐orange▷

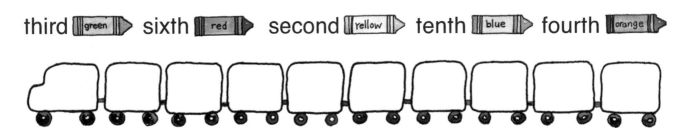

Colour the flowers.

fifth ▐purple▷ seventh ▐red▷ first ▐yellow▷ ninth ▐blue▷ eighth ▐orange▷

FOCUS

Children read and select ordinals first through tenth.

HOME CONNECTION

Talk about the sequence of events in your child's day using first, second, and so on. For example: "First, we eat breakfast."

Name: _____   Date: _____

Days of the Week

Name a day of the week that is special for you.

_____

What day comes 1 day before?

_____

What day comes 1 day after?

_____

What day comes 3 days before?

_____

 FOCUS

Children identify days of the week.

 HOME CONNECTION

Make or mark a calendar with your child. Talk about the family schedule and what happens each day of the week.

Unit 3, Lesson 2: Our Week   **49**

Which Takes Longer?

Look at each pair of pictures.
Circle the one that takes longer.

 FOCUS

Children identify and circle the activity that takes the
longer period of time.

HOME CONNECTION

With your child, talk about activities you do together,
such as grocery shopping and brushing your teeth.
Ask: "Which takes longer?"

Show the Time

Show the time on each clock.

Draw a picture to show what you do at each time.

9 o'clock in the morning		
12 o'clock noon		
4 o'clock in the afternoon		

 FOCUS

Children add hour hands to the clocks to indicate the time and draw pictures to show what they do at those times.

 HOME CONNECTION

Together, draw pictures or write words to show what your child is doing at a time, on the hour, after school. Look at the clock together, and talk about the position of the hour hand.

Name: _____ Date: _____

On the Hour

Write each time.

_____ o'clock

_____ o'clock

_____ o'clock

_____ o'clock

Draw the hour hand.

4 o'clock

nine o'clock

6 o'clock

 FOCUS

Children record and represent time to the hour.

 HOME CONNECTION

Together, record your child's bedtime to the closest hour each night for one week. Review the week's results and ask your child: "Did you go to bed close to the same hour every evening?"

Name: _____ Date: _____

Sort Coins

Sort the coins.

Name: _____ Date: _____

Make 10 Cents

Show three ways to make 10 cents.

10 cents

10 cents

10 cents

Think of another way to make 10 cents.

 FOCUS

Children cut out coins from *Line Master 7: Coins* and paste them in each box to show 10 cents in different ways.

 HOME CONNECTION

Together, make groups of coins, each having a value of 10 cents. Ask your child to look away while you remove a coin from one group. Have your child look at the groups and identify the missing coin.

Dimes, Nickels, Pennies

Record how many cents.

_____ cents

_____ cents

_____ cents

_____ cents

_____ cents

 FOCUS

Children determine and record the total value of the coins in each row.

 HOME CONNECTION

With your child, take turns using pennies and nickels to make groups of coins, each having a value of 10 cents or less. Ask your child to tell you the value, in cents, of each group of coins.

At the Store

What coins would you use?

Can you think of another way?

 FOCUS

Children cut out pictures of coins from *Line Master 7: Coins*. Then they paste them in the children's palms to represent the cost of each item.

 HOME CONNECTION

Have your child name the coins used to represent these money amounts. Then ask, "What other ways can you make these amounts?"

Name: _____   Date: _____

What Is in My Sandwich?

My sandwich costs _____ cents.

 FOCUS

Children choose ingredients from *Line Master 9:*
What Is in My Sandwich? Then they colour, cut out,
and paste ingredients onto the Student page to
make a sandwich that costs up to 10 cents.

 HOME CONNECTION

Ask your child to explain the solution to the problem.

Name: _____ Date: _____

What Is on My Pizza?

My pizza costs _____ cents.

 FOCUS

Children choose toppings from *Line Master 10: What Is on My Pizza?* Then they colour, cut out, and paste toppings onto the Student page to create a pizza that costs up to 10 cents.

 HOME CONNECTION

Ask your child: "What toppings did you choose? Why did you choose those toppings?"

58 Unit 3, Lesson 7: Strategies Tool Kit

Name: _____ Date: _____

The Garage Sale

Cut and paste the pictures in order.

1	**2**
3	**4**

Name: _____ Date: _____

For Sale

Circle the coins to match each tag.
Use as few coins as you can.

FOCUS

Children choose coins to represent money amounts.

HOME CONNECTION

Ask your child to tell you how the activity on this page shows what he or she knows about money. Ask: "How did you decide which coins to use?"

Name: _____ Date: _____

What Will Lu Buy?

Lu has 10 cents.
Circle 2 things she could buy.

 4 cents

 9 cents

 1 cent

 5 cents

 2 cents

How much money did she spend? _____ cents

Show Lu's thinking in pictures, numbers, or words.

 FOCUS

Children circle two objects that Lu can buy with 10 cents. Then they record how much she spent, showing their thinking in pictures, numbers, or words.

 HOME CONNECTION

Ask your child: "Which of these objects would you buy with 10 cents?"

Name: _____ Date: _____

My Journal

Tell what you learned about time, temperature, and money. Use pictures, numbers, or words.

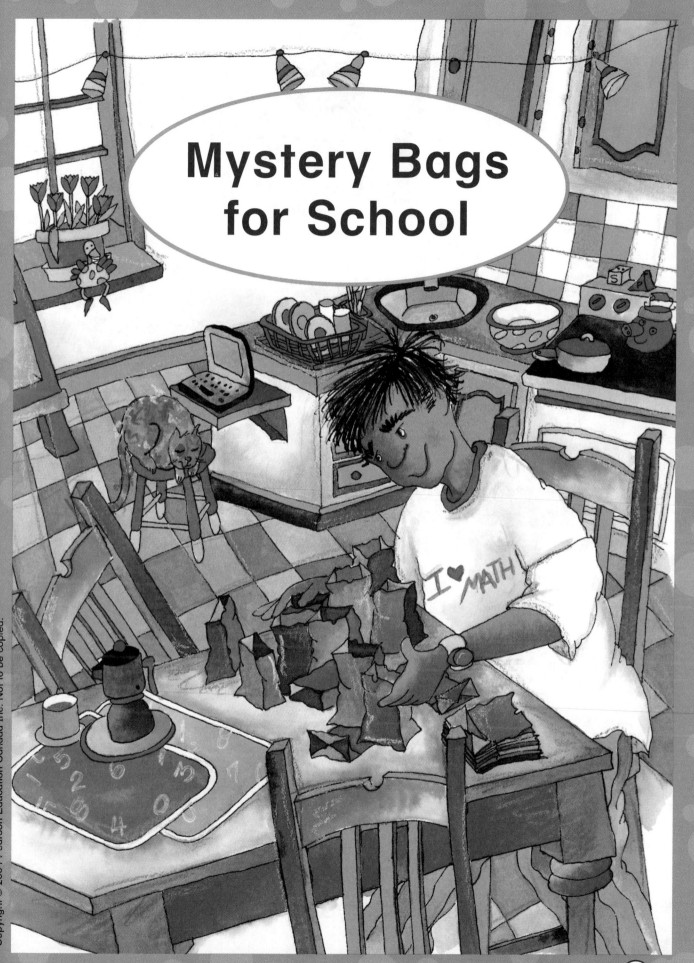

Mystery Bags
for School

I'm making mystery bags for fun.
I need 12 things for everyone.

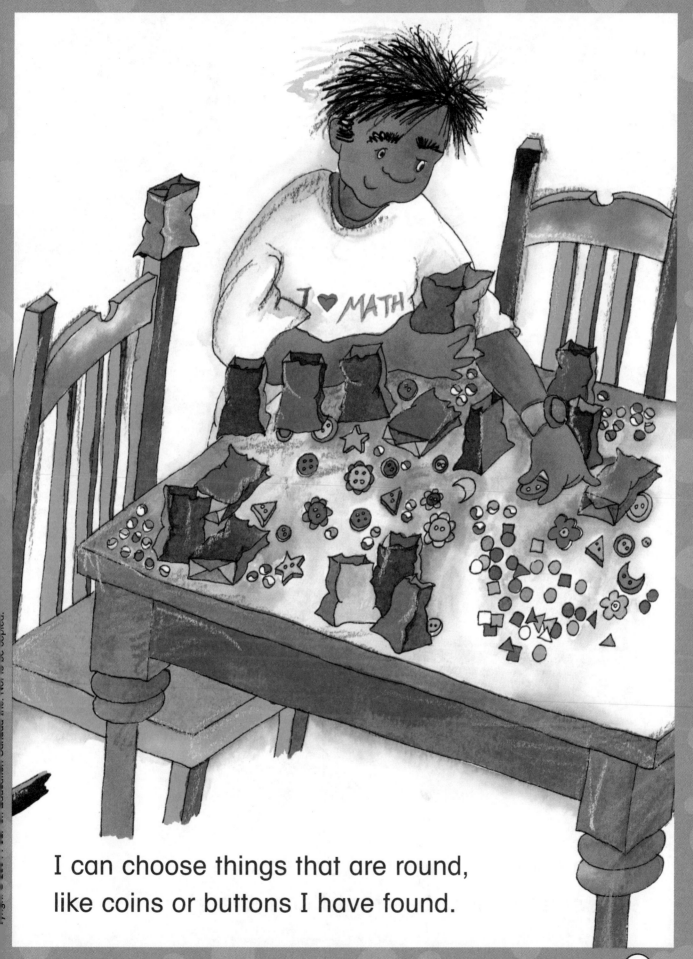

I can choose things that are round,
like coins or buttons I have found.

I can choose things that are square,
like stamps or cubes that I can share.

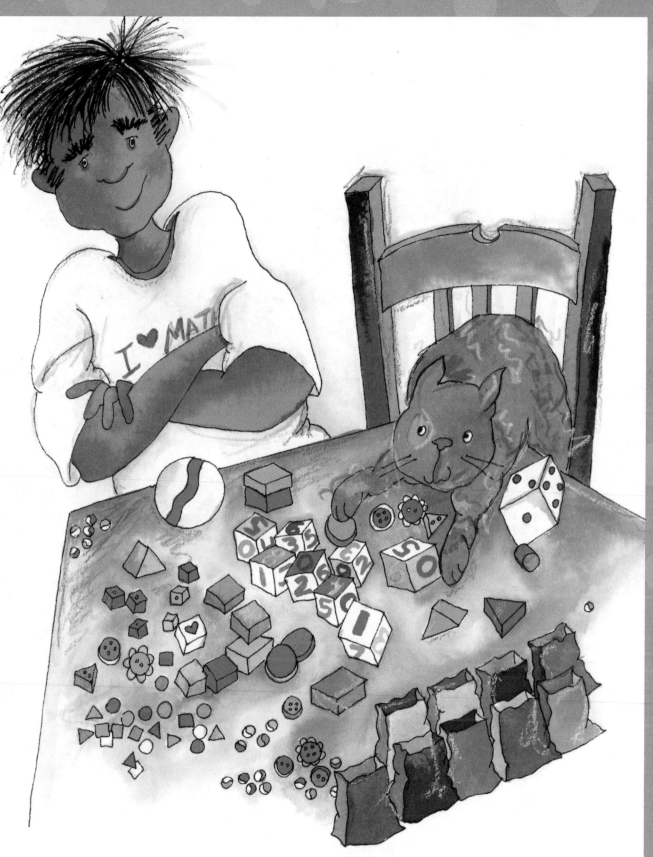

I can choose things red or blue, purple, yellow, orange, too.

I can choose things big or small.
Like marbles or this red-striped ball.

I'll sort these things, then I'll be done.
Mystery bags are lots of fun!

From the Library

Ask the librarian about other good books to share about sorting and patterning, numbers, and measuring time, temperature, and money.

John Burningham, *The Shopping Basket* (William Collins and Sons, 1980)

Eric Carle, *The Grouchy Ladybug* (HarperCollins, 1996)

Phoebe Gilman, *Jillian Jiggs* (Scholastic, 1988)

Tana Hoban, *Let's Count* (Greenwillow Books, 1999)

Bill Martin, Jr., *Brown Bear, Brown Bear, What Do You See?* (Henry Holt and Company, 1992)

Maurice Sendak, *Chicken Soup with Rice: A Book of Months* (HarperCollins, 1991)

Jan Thornhill, *The Wildlife 1-2-3: A Nature Counting Book* (Greey de Pencier, 2003)

Judith Viorst, *Alexander, Who Used to Be Rich Last Sunday* (Simon and Schuster, 1987)

Solve the Mystery!

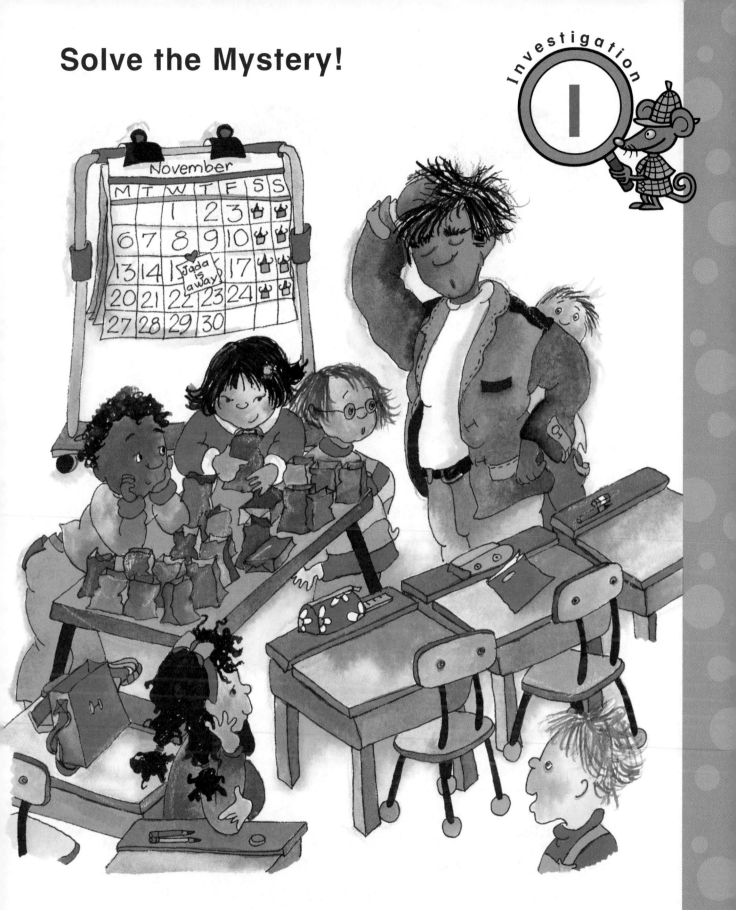

Which bag is Jada's?

How can we help Mr. Gloshes find out?

Do You Have the Special Sorting Bag?

Look in the bag.

Are there more than 10 things?   Yes _____ No _____

Empty the bag.

Show what is inside.

Use pictures, numbers, or words.

Do you have

the special sorting bag?   Yes _____ No _____

Tell a partner about your thinking.

Hint Count everything in the bag.

Sorting!

Sort the objects in your bag.
Show your sorting rule.

Sort a different way.
Show your sorting rule.

 Hint Make a sorting rule.

A Story of 6

Take 6 objects from your bag.
Make a story about your 6 objects.
Use pictures, numbers, or words.

 Tell a story about 6. Show your thinking.

Toy Sort

Gather your favourite toys together in a pile.
Sort them into groups. What's your sorting rule?
When you're done, see if someone can guess your rule.
Now let someone else sort the toys.
It's your turn to guess the rule!

Rainy Day Project

Gather a collection of family pictures.
Put them in order, showing when the pictures were taken.
What picture was taken first?
What picture was taken second?

The next 4 pages fold in half to make an 8-page booklet.

Fold

Math at Home

Math, math, everywhere
You say, "How can that be?"
At home, at school,
and all around,
Just look and you will see.

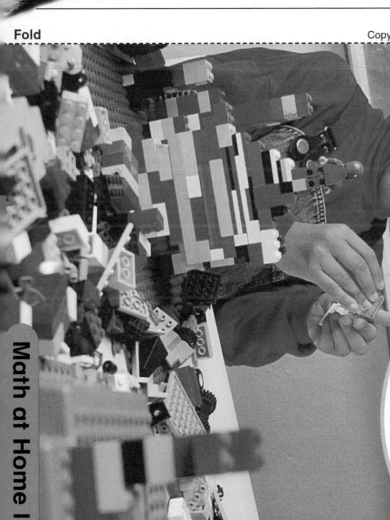

At the Zoo

I see _____ lions.

I see _____ camels.

I see _____ monkeys.

I see _____ zebras.

I see _____ animals
altogether at the zoo.

Number Walk

Someone says a number between 1 and 18.
Everyone hunts for a number "2 more than" that.
The one who finds it first gets to pick a new number.
Now try finding "2 less than" numbers.

Shopping for Numbers

Grocery stores are full of numbers!
How many things can you find
that come in sets of 2? 6? 10? 12?

Setting the Table

How many of each do you need?
Is there a chair for every person?
Is there a knife for every fork?
Is there a plate for every glass?

What if someone else comes to dinner?
How many then?

Trading Game

Game

Be the first to collect 5 dimes.
For 2 players, you'll need:
- 9 pennies, 4 nickels, 9 dimes
- 2 grids like this

Roll a number cube, count the dots,
and take that many pennies.
Place them on your grid.
When one row is full, trade for a nickel.
When you get 2 nickels, trade for a dime.
When you've made all possible trades,
it's your partner's turn.
Keep rolling and trading until you collect 5 dimes.

Another Way
Work as a team to collect 5 dimes!

What's My Rule?

What comes next?
Start a pattern.
Keep adding to it until your partner knows what
the next three parts of the pattern will be.

Now your partner can start a pattern.
It's your turn to guess.

Try: shapes, coins, pasta, buttons, Snap Cubes

A Riddle

What do all of these pictures
have in common?
Can you think of some other object
that belongs with this group?

More or Less Game Board

7	5		7	11	4
4	12	6	12	3	8
11	6	13	9	12	10
3	9	10	7	9	6
8		9	4	5	12
6	8	5	10	7	

How could you make this a "1 less than" game?

Aren't numbers fun?

More Or Less

Game

You'll need:
- Buttons for you
- Buttons for your partner
- 2 number cubes

On your turn:
- Roll 2 number cubes.
- Count all the dots.
- Say the number that is "1 more than" you counted.
- Find the "1 more than" number on the game board.
- Cover it with one of your buttons.

Now it's your partner's turn.

Make Up Your Own Rules

What happens when you can't cover a number?

What will you do with the blank squares?

When is the game over?

UNIT 4

Addition and Subtraction to 12

FOCUS

Children identify the number of bowling pins that are up and down in each lane and practise building number combinations of 5.

HOME CONNECTION

Have your child describe how each lane shows a way to make 5.

Name: _____   Date: _____

Dear Family,

In this unit, your child will be learning about addition and subtraction to 12.

The Learning Goals for this unit are to

- Learn more about the meaning of numbers.
- Recognize that addition involves joining groups and that subtraction involves taking one group away from another.
- Use counters and other real-life materials to help solve simple number problems.
- Practise using addition and subtraction to write and solve number problems.
- Describe the thinking involved in solving simple number problems.

You can help your child reach these goals by doing the activities suggested at the bottom of each page.

Name: _____   Date: _____

10-Pin Bowling

Count the number of pins that are up.
Count the number of pins that are down.
Record the numerals.

_____ up _____ down

_____ up _____ down

_____ up _____ down

_____ up _____ down

_____ up _____ down

_____ up _____ down

 FOCUS

Children identify and write different number
combinations for 10.

 HOME CONNECTION

Have your child describe how each lane shows a
way to make 10.

Unit 4, Launch: Addition and Subtraction to 12   **81**

Name: _____ Date: _____

Number Trains for 5

Use red and blue Snap Cubes.
Colour the cubes. Record the numerals.

_____ □ and _____ □ are _____ □.

_____ □ and _____ □ are _____ □.

_____ □ and _____ □ are _____ □.

_____ □ and _____ □ are _____ □.

_____ □ and _____ □ are _____ □.

_____ □ and _____ □ are _____ □.

 FOCUS

Children make and record different combinations for
5 by colouring cubes, then writing the numerals for
each combination.

 HOME CONNECTION

Have your child explain the activity on this page.
Ask: "Are these all the trains for 5? How do you
know?"

Name: _____ Date: _____

More Number Trains

Use red and blue Snap Cubes.
Colour the cubes. Record the numerals.

Show 4 one way.

_____ ▢ and _____ ▢ are _____ ▢.

Show 4 another way.

_____ ▢ and _____ ▢ are _____ ▢.

Show 7 one way.

_____ ▢ and _____ ▢ are _____ ▢.

Show 7 another way.

_____ ▢ and _____ ▢ are _____ ▢.

Show 9 one way.

_____ ▢ and _____ ▢ are _____ ▢.

Show 9 another way.

_____ ▢ and _____ ▢ are _____ ▢.

 FOCUS

Children build and record different combinations for the same number.

 HOME CONNECTION

Place 3 pennies in a line. Add another line of 3. Say: "I have 3 pennies. I add 3 more. Now I have 6 pennies." Have your child arrange the 6 pennies another way.

Unit 4, Lesson I: Part-Part-Whole (Combining) **83**

Dinosaur Addition Story

Use counters to make an addition story about dinosaurs.
Show your story using pictures, numbers, or words.

_____ and _____ is _____.

FOCUS

Children make a dinosaur addition story using
counters. They show their story in pictures,
numbers, or words.

HOME CONNECTION

Ask your child to tell you the dinosaur story on this
page. Create another addition story together, using
simple objects like buttons or paper clips.

Name: _____   Date: _____

My Addition Story!

Draw or write your story.
Write the addition sentence.

Beginning

There are _____.

Middle

Then _____.

End

_____ and _____ is _____.

 FOCUS

Children use counters to create story problems.
They illustrate or write their stories, ending with the
addition sentence.

HOME CONNECTION

Tell story problems for your child to solve. For
example: "There are 3 spoons on the table. We
need I more. How many spoons do we need all
together?" Say: "3 and I is 4."

More Addition Stories

Record addition sentences.

_____ + _____ = _____

_____ + _____ = _____

  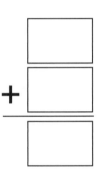

Draw counters to show each addition sentence.

3 + 5 = 8

$\begin{array}{r} 2 \\ + 6 \\ \hline 8 \end{array}$

Make your own addition story. Share it with a partner.

 FOCUS

Children identify, build, and record addition stories.

HOME CONNECTION

Share story problems using objects at home. For example: "6 stuffed animals are playing in the bedroom. 5 more come to play. Now there are 11."

Act Out Addition Stories

Write each number sentence.

_____ + _____ = _____

Name: _____ Date: _____

What Is in the Box?

There are 10 marbles in a box.

Some are green and some are yellow.

There are 2 more yellow marbles than green marbles.

How many yellow marbles are there?

Show your thinking in pictures, numbers, or words.

There are _____ yellow marbles.

 FOCUS

Children figure out a combination of green and yellow marbles that makes 10. They show their solution in pictures, numbers, or words.

 HOME CONNECTION

Ask your child to describe how he or she solved the problem.

Name: _____ Date: _____

What Is in the Bag?

There are 11 balloons in a bag.
Some are red and some are purple.
There are 3 fewer purple balloons than red balloons.

How many purple balloons are there?
Show your thinking in pictures, numbers, or words.

There are _____ purple balloons.

 FOCUS

Children figure out a combination of red and purple
balloons that makes 11. They show their solution in
pictures, numbers, or words.

 HOME CONNECTION

Together, look at the solution your child recorded on
the page. Have your child explain the solution to the
problem.

Unit 4, Lesson 3: Strategies Tool Kit **89**

How Many Are Missing?

Look at the pictures. Record the numerals.

There are _____ ants.　　Now there are _____ ants.

_____ ants went inside.

There are _____ bees.　　Now there are _____ bees.

_____ bees went inside.

 FOCUS

Children build and identify subtraction stories (missing part).

 HOME CONNECTION

Use 10 beads or buttons to play a hiding game. Hide 4 counters in your hand, leaving 6 visible. Ask: "How many are missing?" Repeat, taking turns.

Missing Counters

How many counters does each hand cover?
Record the numerals.

How many are missing? _____   How many are missing? _____

How many are missing? _____   How many are missing? _____

How many are missing? _____   How many are missing? _____

 FOCUS

Children find out how many counters are covered by each hand.

 HOME CONNECTION

Show 8 paper clips. Have your child turn away while you cover some of them with your hand. Ask your child to tell you how many are missing. Repeat, taking turns.

Name: _____   Date: _____

My Subtraction Action Story!

Draw or write your story.
Write the subtraction sentence.

Beginning

There are _____.

Middle

Then _____.

End

_____ take away _____ is _____.

 FOCUS

Children create their own story problems. They
illustrate or write their stories, ending with the
subtraction sentence.

HOME CONNECTION

The best way for your child to learn about subtraction
is by telling subtraction stories. Use real-life situations.
Say: "There are 9 spoons in the drawer. I take out 4
spoons. How many spoons are left in the drawer?"

Subtraction Stories

Write each subtraction sentence.

6 – ____ = ____

6 in a box | Take _____ out.

9 – ____ = ____

9 on the bus | _____ get off.

12 – ____ = ____

12 in the cart | _____ roll out.

 FOCUS

Children identify, build, and record subtraction stories.

 HOME CONNECTION

Ask your child to tell subtraction stories about people in your family. For example: "There are 6 people at home. When I go to school, there are 5 left. 6 take away 1 is 5."

More Subtraction Stories

Use counters to make a subtraction story about children playing together.

Show your story using pictures, numbers, or words.

 FOCUS

Children make a subtraction story using counters. They show their story in pictures, numbers, or words.

HOME CONNECTION

Have your child tell you the story on this page. Ask: "How did you think of that story? How did you decide how many to take away?"

Add or Subtract

Write each number sentence.

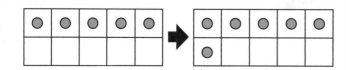

$$\underline{5} \; \bigcirc \; \underline{} = \underline{6}$$

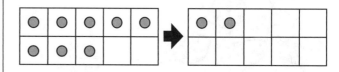

$$\underline{8} \; \bigcirc \; \underline{} = \underline{2}$$

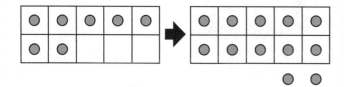

$$\underline{7} \; \bigcirc \; \underline{} = \underline{12}$$

$$\underline{10} \; \bigcirc \; \underline{} = \underline{3}$$

Make Your Own Draw counters. Write a number sentence.

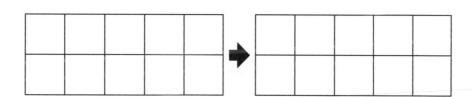

$$\underline{} \; \bigcirc \; \underline{} = \underline{}$$

 FOCUS

Children interpret, build, and record addition and subtraction sentences using ten-frames. Children create their own addition or subtraction sentence using a ten-frame.

 HOME CONNECTION

Together, look at the sentence that your child built and recorded. Ask: "How did you think of that sentence? How did you decide how many to add or take away?"

Unit 4, Lesson 6: Combining and Separating   **95**

Name: _____   Date: _____

Write Number Sentences

Write each number sentence.

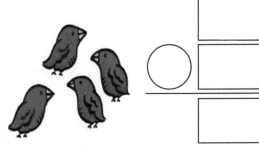

_____ ◯ _____ = _____

_____ ◯ _____ = _____

Make Your Own

_____ ◯ _____ = _____

Make a Number Story

Draw counters to make a number story.
Write a number sentence.

9

3 fly away.

_____ ◯ _____ = _____

7

3 more come.

2

5 jump in.

_____ ◯ _____ = _____

6

6 fly away.

_____ ◯ _____ = _____

 FOCUS

Children draw counters to make number stories.
Then they record a number sentence for each
number story.

 HOME CONNECTION

Ask your child to tell you each number story and read
its number sentence.

Name: _____ Date: _____

My Story of 10

Use pictures, numbers, or words to tell a story of 10.
You can use counters or other objects to help you.

My number sentence is _____ ◯ _____ = _____.

Here is another way I can write it.

FOCUS

Children use pictures, words, and numbers to tell a
number story about 10. Then they write number
sentences for their story.

HOME CONNECTION

Ask your child to tell you the story and read the
number sentences. Ask: "Can you think of another
number story for 10?"

Name: _____ Date: _____

On and Off the Bus!

Write a number sentence to tell what happens each time.

3 children are on the bus.
At the next stop, 5 more get on.

____ ◯ ____ = ____
_____

At the next stop, 4 children get off the bus.

____ ◯ ____ = ____
_____

At the next stop, I child gets off the bus.

____ ◯ ____ = ____
_____

At the last stop, 3 children get off the bus.

____ ◯ ____ = ____
_____

How many children are on the bus now? _____

Name: _____ Date: _____

My Journal

Why are adding and subtracting important?
Use pictures, numbers, or words to show your thinking.

FOCUS

Children reflect on and record what they learned about addition and subtraction in this unit.

HOME CONNECTION

Ask your child: "What do you like best about adding and subtracting? Why do you think addition and subtraction are important?"

Data Management and Probability

 FOCUS

Children talk about different ways to organize data.

 HOME CONNECTION

Look at the picture with your child and talk about how the children are organized.

Name: _____ Date: _____

Dear Family,

In this unit, your child will be learning about making graphs and probability—how likely it is that an event will happen.

The Learning Goals for this unit are to

- Compare, sort, and organize objects into real-life graphs.
- Ask questions, collect, and record gathered information on graphs.
- Read graphs and ask questions about the information on the graphs.
- Decide whether an event will happen *always*, *sometimes*, or *never*.

You can help your child reach these goals by doing the activities suggested at the bottom of each page.

Name: _____ Date: _____

How Are We Sorted?

How many children are wearing stripes? _____

How many are **not** wearing stripes? _____

Where do you belong on the graph? _____

_____

 FOCUS

Children interpret a picture of a concrete graph and tell where they belong on the graph.

HOME CONNECTION

Have your child describe the picture and tell the number of children who are wearing stripes and not wearing stripes. Ask: "If you joined the picture or group, how would it change?"

Unit 5, Launch: Data Management and Probability **103**

My Bean Graph

There are two colours of beans in a bag.
Sort the beans on this graph.

There are _____ more

than .

There are _____ fewer

than .

What does the graph tell you?

 FOCUS

Children sort beans by colour to make a graph and
then interpret the results. Children use colour to
label the graph.

 HOME CONNECTION

Have your child make a graph by sorting small objects
of two colours (red and white paper clips; blue and
green buttons). Use an egg carton as the graphing grid
and talk about what the graph tells you.

104   Unit 5, Lesson I: Build and Interpret Concrete Graphs

Favourite Colours

Use , and to make a graph.

Ask 10 friends to choose the colour they like best.
Colour the graph.

Which colour did your friends like the most? _____

Which colour did your friends like the least? _____

Show your favourite colour on the graph.
Describe to a partner how the graph is different now.

 FOCUS

Children build and interpret a concrete graph.

 HOME CONNECTION

Ask your child to describe the graph. Ask: "What would the graph look like if I add my favourite colour?"

Graphing Names

Ask 6 friends to write their names where they belong.

Less Than 5 Letters	5 Letters	More Than 5 Letters

How many names have less than 5 letters? _____

How many names have 5 letters? _____

How many names have more than 5 letters? _____

Tell a partner a number story about your graph.

FOCUS

Children make a graph of the number of letters in their friends' names and interpret the results.

HOME CONNECTION

Have your child make a name graph using names of family members or other people they know.

Favourite Vegetables

Ask 5 friends to choose their favourite vegetables.
Cut and paste pictures to make a graph.

Which is the favourite vegetable? Tell how you know.
Use pictures, numbers, or words.

Which Do You Like Best?

Which sandwich do most
people like best?

_____

Add the sandwich you like best.
How is the graph different now?

_____

_____

_____

_____

 FOCUS

Children interpret a picture graph. They add their
favourite sandwich to the graph and describe how
the graph has changed.

 HOME CONNECTION

Have your child provide reasons for the change in
the graph after his or her favourite sandwich is
added.

Name: _____ Date: _____

How Many Birthdays?

Do more boys in your class have birthdays
in the summer or during the rest of the year?

Show your thinking in pictures, numbers, or words.

Work with a partner. Make a graph to show how many girls have
birthdays in the summer or during the rest of the year.

 FOCUS

Children work together to use the strategy "make a
graph" to solve a problem.

 HOME CONNECTION

Have your child make a graph to show family
members' or friends' birthdays and whether they
occur in the summer or at other times of the year.

Summer Vacation

Do more children in your class go on
a trip in the summer or stay at home?

Show your thinking in pictures, numbers, or words.

Name: _____ Date: _____

About Our Pets

My Question _____

_____

Ask 10 friends.

Use pictures, numbers, or words to show what you found out.

What do you wonder about?

I wonder _____

_____

FOCUS

Children choose a yes/no question and survey 10 friends.

HOME CONNECTION

Together, talk about the information that your child gathered.

Unit 5, Lesson 4: Conduct a Survey **115**

Name: _____   Date: _____

My Survey

My Question Do you like to _____?

Ask 10 friends. Print their names in the "Yes" or "No" column.

Yes	No

How many friends chose yes? _____

How many friends chose no? _____

FOCUS

Children conduct a survey and record the results.

HOME CONNECTION

Have your child ask up to 10 family members or friends a survey question such as: "Do you like to skate?" or "Do you like to swim?" Together, record the results and create a similar graph.

Name: _____ Date: _____

Favourite Pets

Which pet is the favourite? _____

Which pet is liked the least? _____

How many more people like dogs than cats? _____

How many people in all answered the question? _____

Ask 3 friends to name their favourite pets. Add their answers to the graph. How is the graph different now?

_____

_____

 FOCUS
Children interpret and record responses about a picture graph.

 HOME CONNECTION
Have your child describe and explain the graph.

Unit 5, Lesson 4: Conduct a Survey **II3**

A Story about My Teacher

Use pictures and words.

My teacher always _____.

My teacher sometimes _____.

My teacher never _____.

FOCUS

Children complete sentences and draw matching pictures.

HOME CONNECTION

Have your child talk about events that always, sometimes, or never happen at the library.

Name: _____ Date: _____

At School

Show two things your friends always, sometimes, and never do at school.

Use pictures, numbers, or words.

Always	Sometimes	Never

 FOCUS

Children record two examples of things friends at school always, sometimes, and never do.

HOME CONNECTION

Have your child create a list of things that always, sometimes, and never happen at the library.

My Planning Chart

What do I want to find out?	
What are some questions I could use?	
How many children will I ask?	
How will I record my work?	

 FOCUS

Children prepare a plan for completing the performance task.

HOME CONNECTION

Talk with your child about the plan for the task. Ask: "How did the plan help you?"

Name: _____ Date: _____

Would You Rather ...?

My Question _____

_____

Predict which answer will be the favourite choice. _____
Show what you found out.

[ ]

What did you find out? _____

If you asked 5 different people, would you always get the same
answer? Why?

FOCUS
Children work in groups to conduct a survey and to
record and interpret the results.

HOME CONNECTION
Have your child choose a survey question to ask
family members or neighbours.

Name: _____ Date: _____

My Journal

What did I learn about graphing?
Use pictures, numbers, or words.

FOCUS
Children reflect on and record what they learned about graphing.

HOME CONNECTION
Have your child choose a favourite activity from the unit and tell you why it was a favourite.

118 **Unit 5, Lesson 6:** Show What You Know

Copyright © 2004 Pearson Education Canada Inc. **Not to be copied.**

UNIT 6

3-D and 2-D Geometry

 FOCUS

Children find and describe 3-D solids in this picture.

 HOME CONNECTION

Ask your child to describe the 3-D solids that make up the castle.

Name: _____   Date: _____

Dear Family,

In this unit, your child will be learning about geometry.

The Learning Goals for this unit are to

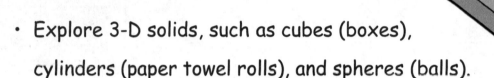

- Explore 3-D solids, such as cubes (boxes), cylinders (paper towel rolls), and spheres (balls).
- Describe 3-D solids. For example, some solids can roll, some have points, some are curved, and some can stack.
- Make a picture using 2-D figures, such as triangles or rectangles.
- Use language, such as *on, in, under,* and *over* to describe where objects are placed.

You can help your child reach these goals by doing the activities suggested at the bottom of each page.

Castle Detectives

Colour a red.

Colour a blue.

Colour a green.

Colour a orange.

Colour a yellow.

FOCUS

Children find and colour the matching 3-D solids.

HOME CONNECTION

Go on a neighbourhood walk with your child. Talk about the geometric solids (cone, cube, cylinder, sphere, rectangular prism) you see in buildings and different settings.

Our Tall Tower

We built a tall tower.

Solids	How Many Solids?

We used _____ solids in all.

We put a _____ on the bottom.

We put a _____ on the top.

 FOCUS

Children record the solids they used to build a tower. Later, they will compare results with other groups.

HOME CONNECTION

Have your child experiment by building tall towers out of blocks, small boxes, cans, or other household objects.

Name: _____ Date: _____

Our Friends' Tall Tower

What 3-D solids can you see?

Solids	How Many Solids?

How is your friends' tower different from your tower?

Use pictures, numbers, or words.

FOCUS

Children record the solids their friends used to build a tower and compare that tower with their own.

HOME CONNECTION

With your child, collect 3-D solids to use with this unit: cones (party hats), cylinders (cans, toilet-tissue rolls), rectangular prisms (cereal boxes, milk cartons), spheres (balls), and cubes (square boxes).

Name: _____ Date: _____

I Am a Builder

3-D Solids	My Tower

 FOCUS

Children use all the solids shown to build a structure. They record their creations by cutting and pasting solid pictures from *Line Master 3: 3-D Solids*.

 HOME CONNECTION

Have your child create an imaginary creature by taping together 3-D solids you collected (party hats, cans, toilet tissue rolls, and so on).

Name: _____   Date: _____

The Sorting Game

Play the game with a partner.
Can your partner guess your rule?

All of these _____.   None of these _____.

 FOCUS

Children record their sorting rule. They paste or
draw pictures of solids into the two boxes to show
how they sorted the solids.

 HOME CONNECTION

Have your child explain the sorting rule. Together,
find some cans, sugar cubes, boxes, and marbles.
Then decide which group each belongs in.

Unit 6, Lesson 2: Attributes of 3-D Solids

Name: _____ Date: _____

My 3-D Solids Chart

Use a ✔ or ✘ .

	sphere ⬤	cylinder ▭	cube ⬜	cone △
It rolls.				
It has corners.				
It stacks.				

In real life, where do you see △ ▭ ⬤ ◻ ▭ ?
Share your thinking with a partner.

 FOCUS

Children think about each solid. If the solid has the attribute listed at the left, they put a ✔. If not, they mark an ✘.

 HOME CONNECTION

Ask your child to choose an object from your home collection and describe it using words such as *rolls, has corners*, or *stacks*.

Name: _____ Date: _____

Sorting Solids

Sort and paste pictures.

These can stack.	These can roll.
These have points.	**These have flat sides.**

 FOCUS

Children cut out pictures of solids from *Line Master 3: 3-D Solids*. Then they sort the solids based on their attributes and paste them into a chart.

 HOME CONNECTION

Gather a collection of different 3-D solids. Ask your child to find all the objects that can stack and to name the 3-D solids.

In Our Picture

We made a picture of a _____ .

Figure	How Many?
●	
▲	
■	
▬	

We used _____ figures in all.

Which figure did you use the most? _____

Which figure did you use the least? _____

Make a Person

Cut out figures. Use the figures to make a person.

Figure	How Many?
●	
■	
▬	
▲	

FOCUS

Children cut out 2-D figures from *Line Master 6: Cut-Out Figures*, then arrange and paste them to make a person.

HOME CONNECTION

Help your child find 2-D figures—triangles, squares, rectangles, and circles—in your home and draw them on a sheet of paper.

Unit 6, Lesson 3: Create a Picture

Name: _____ Date: _____

Guess My Picture

Make a picture with 2-D figures.

I made a _____.

 FOCUS

Children create pictures with Pattern Blocks and then record the pictures by cutting and pasting figures from *Line Master 7: Pattern Block Figures*.

 HOME CONNECTION

With your child, look for pictures in a flyer, magazine, or newspaper. Ask: "How many triangles can we find? circles? squares? rectangles?"

Where Is the Object?

Choose the best word to fill in the blanks.

on	under	left	beside	
in	over	right	front	behind

The is _____ the beach.

The is to the _____ of the treasure box.

The is to the _____ of the treasure box.

The is in _____ of the treasure box.

The is _____ the treasure box.

 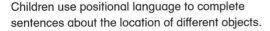

FOCUS

Children use positional language to complete sentences about the location of different objects.

HOME CONNECTION

Hide an object. Sketch a "treasure map" or give oral directions, using the words above to lead your child to the object.

Unit 6, Lesson 4: Spatial Awareness

Name: _____   Date: _____

Place Your Name

Ravi Tara Jake

Print your name under the circle.	Print your name over the rectangle.
Print your name to the right of the triangle.	Print your name beside the square.

 FOCUS

Children read positional language and write their names in the appropriate positions.

 HOME CONNECTION

Play "Simon Says" with positional language. Simon says: "Hold the cup over the table." Simon says: "Put the paper under the chair." Take turns playing Simon.

Draw a Picture

Draw:

- a ● beside .

- a ▲ over .

- a ▭ to the left of .

- a ■ under .

FOCUS

Children follow directions to draw figures in specified positions.

HOME CONNECTION

Play board games with your child. Following directions, such as "move back two spaces," will help reinforce your child's spatial awareness.

Unit 6, Lesson 4: Spatial Awareness   **133**

Let's Solve a Problem

Put the   in order.

Read the clues.

The is on the top.

The is above the .

The is not on the bottom.

The is below the .

Show how you solved the problem.

FOCUS

Children use the clues to put the 3-D solids in a specified order, then record their work.

HOME CONNECTION

Invite your child to tell you what this problem is and how he or she solved it.

Name: _____ Date: _____

Solve This Problem!

Put the [rectangular prism] [rectangular prism] [cone] [cylinder] in order.

Read the clues.

The [cube] is on the bottom.

The [rectangular prism] is above the [cube].

The [cylinder] is below the [cone].

The [cylinder] is on top of the [rectangular prism].

Show how you solved the problem.

FOCUS
Children use the clues to put the 3-D solids in a specified order, then record their work.

HOME CONNECTION
Invite your child to explain the clues in this problem and tell how he or she solved the problem.

Same and Different

Look at your castle. Look at the teacher's castle.

Show your thinking in pictures, numbers, or words.

How are they the same?

How are they different?

FOCUS

Children follow directions to build a castle and then compare it to another castle.

HOME CONNECTION

Set out pairs of household objects, such as a can and a paper towel roll, and ask your child to tell how they are the same and how they are different.

Hiding an Object

You can use pictures or words.

Describe where you hid an object in your castle.

Describe where you found the object in someone else's castle.

 FOCUS

Children show how they hid a secret object in their castle and tell about the object they found in another castle.

HOME CONNECTION

Hide an object in your home. Give clues to its location and invite your child to hunt for it.

Name: _____ Date: _____

My Journal

What did you learn about solids?
Show your thinking.

What did you learn about figures?
Show your thinking.

 FOCUS

Children reflect on what they learned about 3-D solids and 2-D figures in this unit.

HOME CONNECTION

Ask your child to describe a favourite activity from the unit. Ask: "Why is it your favourite?"

Number Patterns

 FOCUS

Children identify and use patterns to predict the next item or number in a sequence.

 HOME CONNECTION

Have your child tell you about the patterns on this page. Ask: "What do you think will come next? How did you decide what would come next?"

Name: _____   Date: _____

Dear Family,

In this unit, your child will be learning more about numbers to 50 and addition and subtraction to 20.

The Learning Goals for this unit are to

- Explore number patterns.
- Estimate and count large collections of objects (up to 50).
- Use a calculator to skip count.
- Explore "doubles" (for example, 2 + 2, 3 + 3).
- Solve simple addition and subtraction problems.

You can help your child reach these goals by doing the activities suggested at the bottom of each page.

Counting Ears

How many ears do 8 rabbits have?

Record the pattern.

Show how you got your answer.

 FOCUS

Children use patterns to help them determine the
number of ears on 8 rabbits. They record their
pattern and show how they solved the problem.

HOME CONNECTION

With your child, search together in your home for
things that come in 2's, and practise counting them
(2-4-6-8-10).

Name: _____   Date: _____

Number Mystery

Fill in the missing numerals.

1	2	3	4		6	7	8	9	10
11	12	13	14				18	19	20
21	22		24	25	26	27	28	29	30
31	32			35	36	37	38	39	
	42	43	44	45	46	47	48	49	

Share your chart with a partner.

Talk about how you found the missing numerals.

 FOCUS
Children fill in the missing numerals on the 50-chart.

 HOME CONNECTION
Show your child a page number (between 20 and 50) in a book or magazine. Ask: "What will the next page number be? What page number came before?" Repeat with different pages.

Name: _____ Date: _____

Count Two Ways

Spill the objects.

Estimate the number. _____

Count the objects.

Show how you counted. Use pictures, numbers, or words.

Spill the objects again. Count them another way.

Show how you counted. Use pictures, numbers, or words.

 FOCUS

Children count a collection of objects in two different ways. They record their counting methods using pictures, numbers, or words.

 HOME CONNECTION

Gather up to 50 pennies or other small objects. Ask your child to show you two different ways of counting them.

Name: _____ Date: _____

Groups of I0's

Estimate the number of fish. _____
Circle groups of I0's.

How many groups of I0's? _____ How many left over? _____

How many in all? _____

_____

Estimate the number of fish. _____
Circle groups of I0's.

How many groups of I0's? _____ How many left over? _____

How many in all? _____

 FOCUS

Children estimate, then group by I0's to find the number of fish.

 HOME CONNECTION

Put up to 50 small objects such as pennies, into a container, but don't tell your child how many there are. Have your child spill the objects, estimate the number, then put them in groups of I0's to count them.

Numbers to 50

Circle groups of 10's. Record the numerals.

_____ 10's and _____   _____ in all

_____ 10's and _____   _____ in all

_____ 10's and _____   _____ in all

 FOCUS

Children circle groups of 10's to help count large numbers of objects.

HOME CONNECTION

Ask your child to explain how grouping by 10's helps to count large numbers of objects.

Unit 7, Lesson 2: Counting Collections   **145**

What Is the Pattern?

Use counters to make a number pattern.
Then show your number pattern.
Use pictures, numbers, or words.

FOCUS

Children use counters to make a number pattern.
They show their pattern in pictures, numbers, or
words.

HOME CONNECTION

Together, look at the number pattern your child
recorded. Ask: "How can you describe the pattern?"
Create another number pattern using simple objects
such as buttons or pennies.

Name: _____ Date: _____

A Counting Pattern

How many fish?

_____ fish

_____ fish

_____ fish

_____ fish

_____ fish

What if the pattern continues? How many fish will be in II bowls?
Use pictures, numbers, or words to show your answer.

<table>
<tr><td>

</td></tr>
</table>

 FOCUS

Children use a growing number pattern to predict
the number of fish there will be in II fishbowls.
They show their answer using pictures, numbers,
or words.

 HOME CONNECTION

Your child is learning about number patterns. Make
up problems that can be solved by counting by 2's.
For example, ask: "How can we find out how many
socks there are in I0 pairs?"

Unit 7, Lesson 3: Counting Patterns   **147**

How Many?

Count by 2's. Record the numerals.

2   4   6   _____   _____   _____

Count by 5's. Record the numerals.

5   10   15   _____   _____   _____

Count by 10's. Record the numerals.

10   20   30   _____   _____   _____

 FOCUS

Children identify each counting pattern and record the missing numerals.

 HOME CONNECTION

Ask your child to explain how he or she counted the items in each row.

Name: _____ Date: _____

Counting on a Calculator

Count by 2's.
Press the keys. Print the numerals you see.

_____   _____

_____   _____

Count by 10's.
Press the keys. Print the numerals you see.

_____   _____

_____   _____

 FOCUS

Children use a calculator to count by 2's and 10's.
They record the numerals that appear on the
screen.

 HOME CONNECTION

If you have a calculator at home, ask your child to
teach you how to use it to skip count by 2's and 10's.

Unit 7, Lesson 4: Skip Counting on the Calculator

Name: _____ Date: _____

What Is the Counting Pattern?

Start at 3. Count by 2's.
Press the keys.

| ON/C | 3 | + | 2 | = | = | = | = |

Record the pattern.

_____

What is the pattern rule?

_____

Start at 7. Count by 10's.
Press the keys.

| ON/C | 7 | + | 1 | 0 | = | = | = | = |

Record the pattern.

_____

What is the pattern rule?

_____

 FOCUS

Children count by 2's and 10's from different start numbers on the calculator. They record the patterns and the pattern rules.

 HOME CONNECTION

If you have a home calculator, take turns skip counting. Start at different numbers. Together, chant the numbers aloud as they appear on screen.

Name: _____ Date: _____

How Many Wheels?

We are building 5 bicycles.

How many wheels will we need?

Show your thinking in pictures, numbers, or words.

Name: _____ Date: _____

How Many Bicycles?

A bicycle rack holds 5 bicycles.
The school has 4 bicycle racks.
How many bicycles can be parked?

Show your thinking in pictures, numbers, or words.

FOCUS

Children use a pattern to solve a problem. They express their solutions in pictures, numbers, or words.

HOME CONNECTION

Have your child explain how he or she solved this problem. Ask: "How did you know the number of bicycles? Tell me about your thinking."

Name: _____ Date: _____

Domino Doubles

Write the number sentences.

_____ + _____ = _____

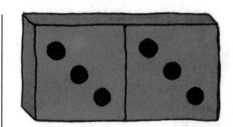

_____ + _____ = _____

_____ + _____ = _____

_____ + _____ = _____

Make Your Own

_____ + _____ = _____

 FOCUS

Children write addition sentences to describe the doubles facts illustrated. They draw their own dominoes to reflect a doubles fact and record the matching addition sentence.

 HOME CONNECTION

With your child, take turns drawing from playing cards. The first one to pick up doubles tells an addition story. "I have double 4's. 4 knights are in a castle and 4 more come. Now there are 8. 4 + 4 is 8."

Unit 7, Lesson 6: Doubles   **153**

Tell a Doubles Story

Tell addition stories.

Write the number sentences.

_____ + _____ = _____

_____ + _____ = _____

_____ + _____ = _____

 FOCUS

Children write number sentences and tell addition stories about doubles facts.

 HOME CONNECTION

Ask your child to tell a number story about each doubles fact illustrated.

Name: _____ Date: _____

Add with Doubles

Use counters. Write the addition story.

_____ + _____ = _____

_____ + _____ = _____

_____ + _____ = _____

_____ + _____ = _____

Use doubles. Draw a picture. Write the addition story.

Make Your Own

 FOCUS

Children use counters to make and record doubles facts. They draw a picture of their own doubles fact and record the matching addition story.

 HOME CONNECTION

Ask your child to think of something at home that comes in doubles (for example, pairs of socks, pairs of shoes).

Addition and Subtraction Stories

Tell an addition story.

My addition sentence _____ **+** _____ **=** _____

Tell a subtraction story.

My subtraction sentence _____ **−** _____ **=** _____

Number Sentences

Write each number sentence.

6 children have .

7 more children get caps, too.   _____ ⃝ _____ = _____

17 are on a shelf.

6 fall off.   _____ ⃝ _____ = _____

13 are standing by the fence.

7 fall over.   _____ ⃝ _____ = _____

14 are on a bench.

6 more are in a box.   _____ ⃝ _____ = _____

FOCUS

Children write number sentences about the pictures shown.

HOME CONNECTION

Have your child tell about one of the number sentences recorded on the page. Ask: "How did you think of that number sentence? How did you decide how many to add or take away?"

Name: _____ Date: _____

Add or Subtract

Use counters. Write each number sentence.

There are 16 .

2 more come.
How many are there in all?

_____ ◯ _____ = _____

There are 17 .

8 fly away.
How many are there now?

_____ ◯ _____ = _____

There are 12 .

6 fly away.
How many are there now?

_____ ◯ _____ = _____

There are 5 .

7 join them.

_____ ◯ _____ = _____

How many are there in all?

 FOCUS

Children use counters to represent each addition or subtraction story and record matching number sentences.

 HOME CONNECTION

Ask your child to explain the solutions to the number stories on the page.

By the River

What's happening by the river?

Make an addition story

_____ ◯ _____ = _____

Make a subtraction story

_____ ◯ _____ = _____

FOCUS

Children tell addition and subtraction stories about animals in the rainforest.

HOME CONNECTION

Pose story problems about things you and your child see or do. For example: "There are 9 juice boxes on the shelf. There are 3 juice boxes on the counter. How many juice boxes are there in all?"

Unit 7, Lesson 8: Posing and Solving Story Problems **159**

Be a Problem Solver

Solve each problem.

There are 4 . There are 7 .
How many kittens in all?

There are _____ in all.

19 are in a pen. 6 run away.

How many are in the pen?

_____ rabbits are in the pen.

Tell a number story to go with the picture. Write a number sentence.

_____ ◯ _____ = _____

 FOCUS

Children use pictures, numbers, or words to solve
addition and subtraction story problems.

 HOME CONNECTION

Share addition and subtraction story problems using
things you see in your neighbourhood. For example,
"14 cars are parked on the street. 3 cars are red. How
many cars are not red?"

Neighbourhood Party

There is a party on Oak Street.
12 girls are coming. 8 boys are coming.

The grown-ups are making a hat for each child at the party.
How many hats should they make?

They should make _____ party hats.

The grown-ups are blowing up a balloon for each child.
They blow up 15 balloons.
How many more balloons do they need?

They need _____ more balloons.

FOCUS

Children solve number-story problems to show what they learned about addition and subtraction.

HOME CONNECTION

These problems give your child a chance to show what he or she learned about addition and subtraction to 20. Have your child explain the solution to each problem.

Surprise Bags

Remember!
12 girls are coming.
8 boys are coming.

The grown-ups make a party bag for each child at the party.
Each bag will get 2 stickers.
How many stickers do they need?

Show your thinking in pictures, numbers, or words.

They need _____ stickers.

FOCUS

Children solve a number-story problem to show what they learned about patterns.

HOME CONNECTION

Together, look at the solution your child recorded on the page. Ask your child to explain the solution to the problem. Ask: "How many stickers would be needed if each child received 3 stickers?"

Party Games

Some children play tug-that-rope at the party.
There are 9 children on each team.
How many children play?

Show your thinking in pictures, numbers, or words.

Make up your own problem about the party.
Then use pictures, numbers, or words to solve it.

FOCUS

Children solve a story problem that involves doubles. Then they create their own addition or subtraction problem.

HOME CONNECTION

Create and solve other "party problems" like the ones shown. Provide paper for drawing and small objects for trying out solutions.

My Journal

Tell what you learned about number patterns.
Use pictures, numbers, or words.

Tell what you learned about addition and subtraction to 20.
Use pictures, numbers, or words.

 FOCUS
Children reflect on and record what they learned
about number patterns and addition and subtraction
in this unit.

HOME CONNECTION
Ask your child: "What did you learn about number
patterns? Why do you think they are important? What
did you learn about addition and subtraction to 20?"

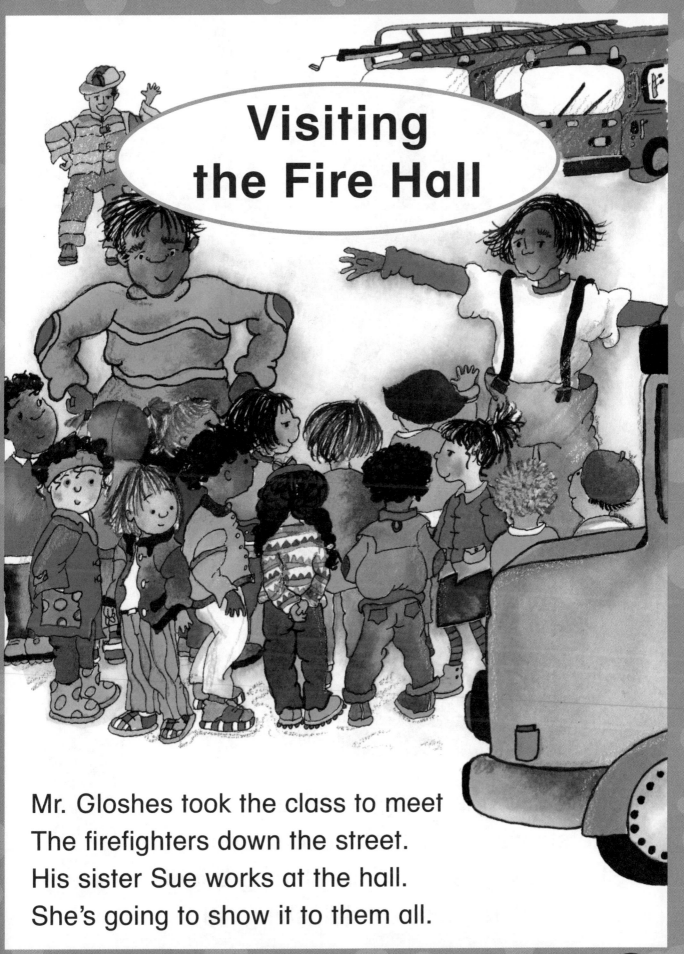

Visiting the Fire Hall

Mr. Gloshes took the class to meet
The firefighters down the street.
His sister Sue works at the hall.
She's going to show it to them all.

She shows the firefighters' suits.
She shows the helmets, coats, and boots.
She shows the red truck, shining bright.
With ladders, hose, and flashing light.

Suddenly a message is phoned through.
A man shouts, "Sue, this one's for you."
"I have to go," Sue tells them all.
"We have an emergency rescue call."

"There is a cat stuck in a tree.
It's a very special cat, you see.
We won't be long. It isn't far.
So wait for us. Stay where you are."

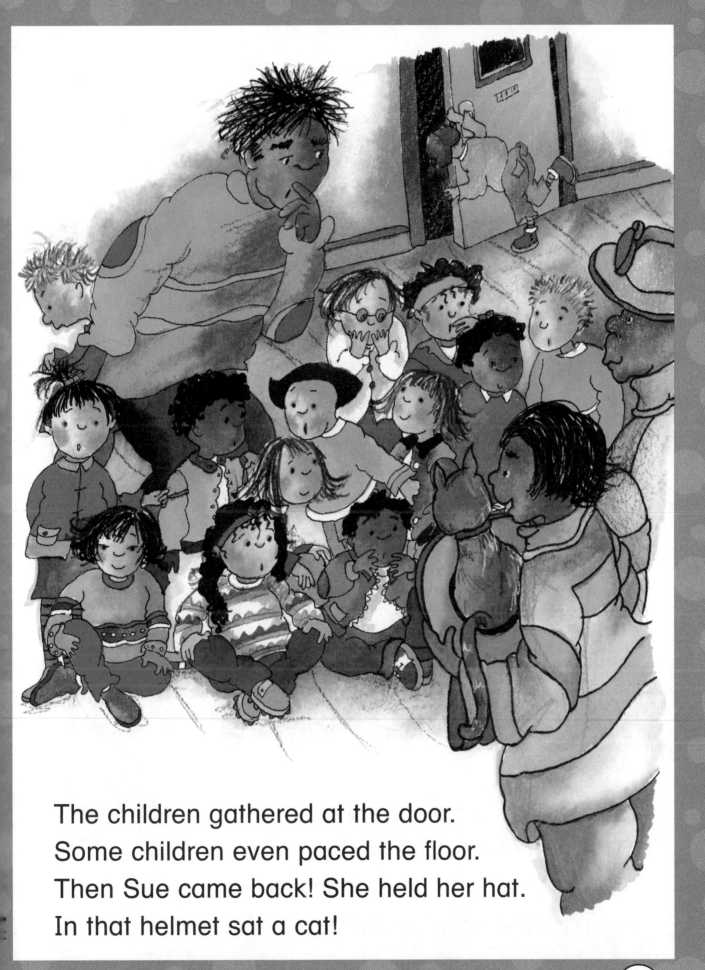

The children gathered at the door.
Some children even paced the floor.
Then Sue came back! She held her hat.
In that helmet sat a cat!

Mr. Gloshes eyes were wide.

"That's my cat!" Mr. Gloshes cried.

"Thank you for bringing him back to me.

I don't know how he climbed that tree."

"You're welcome," said his sister Sue.

"Helping out is what we do."

"Give a cheer—hip, hip hooray!

Firefighters save the day!"

From the Library

Ask the librarian about other books to share about numbers, collecting, sorting, and analyzing information, things that happen *sometimes*, *always*, and *never*, and geometric shapes.

Suzanne Aker, *What Comes in 2's, 3's, and 4's?*
(Aladdin Library, 1992)

Rhonda Gowler Greene, *When a Line Bends...A Shape Begins*
(Houghton Mifflin, 2001)

Ann Grifalconi, *The Village of Round and Square Houses*
(Little Brown, 1986)

Tana Hoban, *Cubes, Cones, Cylinders, and Spheres*
(Greenwillow, 2000)

Caren Holtzman, *No Fair!* (Cartwheel Books, 1997)

Simon James, *Dear Mr. Blueberry* (Aladdin Library, 1996)

Laura Joffe Numeroff, *If You Give a Moose a Muffin*
(Scott Foresman, 1991)

At the Fire Hall

Make number stories about the picture.

Fire Hall Number Stories

Use your counters to make
an addition story about the fire hall.
Use pictures, numbers, or words.
Write an addition sentence for your story.

My story

My addition sentence _____

Make a subtraction story, too.

My story

My subtraction sentence _____

Hint Count the objects and people in the picture.

Our Favourite Rescue Helpers

Make your prediction.

Which one will be the favourite? _____

Which one will be second? _____

Look at your graph.
Write a sentence about what you see.

_____

_____

_____

_____

_____

 Hint Compare the number of pictures in each column.

Our Rescue Tower

Take 6 objects from your bag.
Make a story about your 6 objects.
Use pictures, numbers, or words.

Show your rescue tower.

What We Used	How Many?
(cube)	
(rectangular prism)	
(cone)	
(sphere)	

 Hint Think about 3-D objects that stack.

Hide and Seek

Hide an object, then have a friend
try to find your object.
Use only words like *right*, *left*, *forwards*, *back*,
and *under* as clues.
Now switch places and let your friend guess.
What do you think?
Did the special words you used help you?

Out for a Drive

Have you ever heard someone say,
"I always get ALL the red lights!"?
It's time to see if they're right.
Next time you're out driving,
grab a piece of paper and a pencil
and mark each time the car stops
at a red light or goes through a green one.
What do you think you'll find out?

Fold

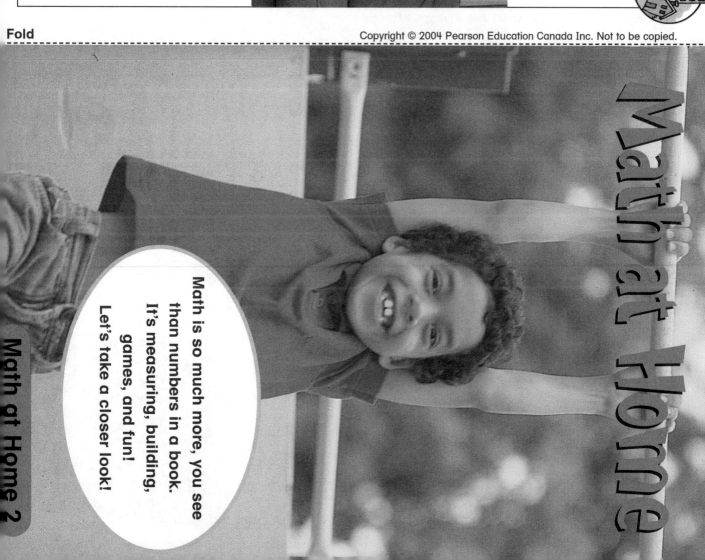

Math at Home

Math is so much more, you see
than numbers in a book.
It's measuring, building,
games, and fun!
Let's take a closer look!

Math at Home 2

Doubles Rap

1 and 1 is _____   Just to name a few.

2 and 2 is _____   Stomp right out that door.

3 and 3 is _____   Add more to the mix.

4 and 4 is _____   Hurry! Don't be late.

5 and 5 is _____   Time to start again.

Read, rap, and sing the poem
a few times.
Use counters to show
each addition sentence
found in the poem.
Use the doubles facts
to help you solve the problems below.

You know that

2 + 2 is 4   So, 2 + 3 is _____

4 + 4 is 8   So, 4 + 5 is _____

Make up more on your own.
How could the doubles facts help you subtract?

Doubles Hunt

Look in a mirror and search
for all the parts of your body
that come in groups of 2's.
How many can you see?
Just find out by
counting by 2's!

Paste a Picture

Grab a handful of toasted O's cereal
and sort the pieces of cereal into groups of 10's.
Count by 10's to see how many pieces you have.

- Use the cereal to make
  a picture on a piece
  of brightly coloured paper.
- Glue each piece of cereal
  to the paper.
- Finally, name your
  piece of art.
  (Don't forget to print
  how many pieces
  of cereal you used
  to make your masterpiece!)

43

Graph-a-Shoe

Ever wonder what type of shoe is most popular at your home?

Well, wonder no more!

It's time to find out!

- Gather all the shoes together and put them in a big pile.
- Sort them into groups.
  You might look at whether they are laced, have buckles, or have Velcro. You decide.
- Put your piles in straight rows to make a graph.

Talk about what you notice.

Which row has the most shoes? The least?

Are you surprised?

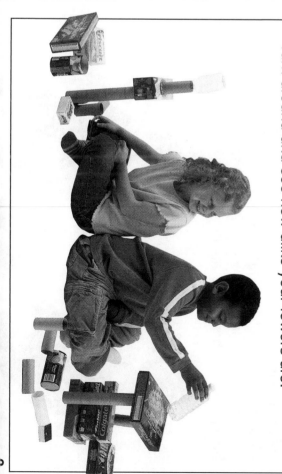

Build a Tower

You'll need:
- lots of 3-D objects

How to play:
- Sit back-to-back with a partner.
- Build a tower using at least eight 3-D objects.
- Give your partner careful directions, explaining how to build a tower the same as yours. No peeking!

All done?

Turn around and see how alike your towers are.

Parking Lot Game Boards

Park-a-Lot Game

Game

You'll need:
- 12 small toy cars (or any small objects)
- one number cube
- the parking lot game boards on the following page

On your turn:
- Roll the number cube.
- Count the dots.
- Park the car in the matching spot. (If you roll a 2, you park your car in the second spot.)

Now, it's your partner's turn.
If you roll a spot and a car is already parked there, miss your turn.
When your lot is full, the game is over.
Could you play this game with 12 parking spots?
How many number cubes would you need?

Linear Measurement and Area

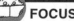 **FOCUS**

Children talk about measuring at home, at school, and in the community.

 HOME CONNECTION

Invite your child to describe the pictures. Ask: "What are these people doing? What do they want to find out? Why is it important to measure these things?"

Dear Family,

In this unit, your child will be learning about linear measurement and area.

The Learning Goals for this unit are to

- Make comparisons between objects (longer, taller).
- Order lengths of objects (shortest to longest).
- Measure common objects using non-standard units such as a paper clip, a pencil, or a sheet of newspaper.
- Practise the language of measurement using words such as *longer/shorter, as tall as, more/less, far/near.*
- Make and check estimates. (Which one is longer? How many things will be needed to cover this?)

You can help your child reach these goals by doing the activities suggested at the bottom of each page.

Name: _____ Date: _____

I Can Measure

Show what you are measuring.

I measured _____ .

I found out _____

_____ .

 FOCUS

Children draw pictures of themselves measuring, sharing what they measured and what they found out.

 HOME CONNECTION

Have your child describe the picture. Talk about what measurements are made at home, such as heights on a growth chart or the length or width of a window.

Longer or Shorter?

Which object is longer? Which object is shorter?

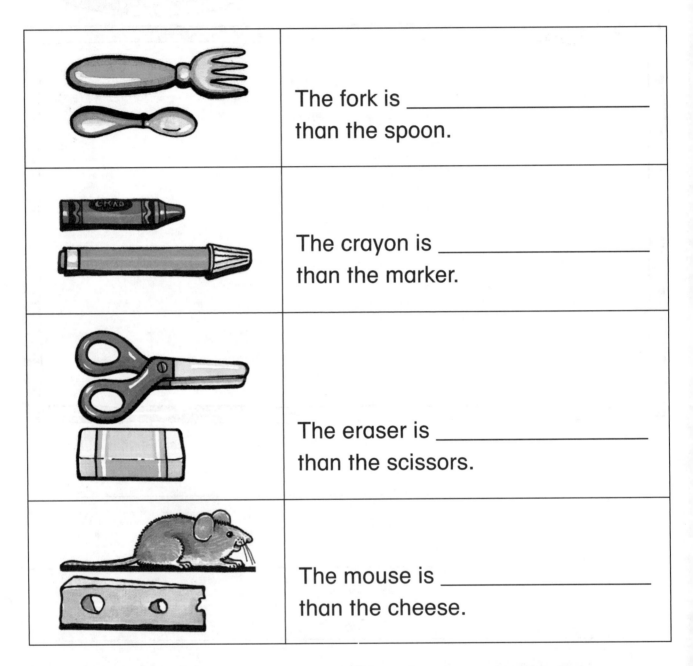

The fork is _____ than the spoon.

The crayon is _____ than the marker.

The eraser is _____ than the scissors.

The mouse is _____ than the cheese.

 FOCUS
Children compare lengths of objects.

HOME CONNECTION
Ask your child to compare the lengths of different objects at home (for example, a child's shoe and an adult's shoe).

Name: _____ Date: _____

Measurement Hunt!

Use 5 Snap Cubes to make a train.

Draw an object that is shorter than the train.

The _____ is shorter.

Draw an object that is longer than the train.

The _____ is longer.

Draw an object that is about as long as the train.

The _____ is about as long.

 FOCUS

Children compare lengths using non-standard units.

HOME CONNECTION

Choose a unit, like a spoon, and find objects that are shorter, longer, and about the same length. Choose a different unit and measure the same items. Ask: "Why did we get different answers?"

Name: _____ Date: _____

Measure How Tall

Friend	Estimate	Measure
	about _____	_____
	about _____	_____
	about _____	_____
	about _____	_____

 FOCUS

Children use a non-standard unit to estimate, measure, and record the heights of four friends.

HOME CONNECTION

Using straws, pencils, or string, work with your child to estimate the height of each family member. Have your child measure to check the estimates.

Estimate, Measure, and Record

Use 5 Snap Cubes to make a train.
Use the train to estimate and measure 4 objects.

Object	Estimate	Measure
Chalk brush	about _____	_____
Desktop	about _____	_____
Book cover	about _____	_____
(My Object)	about _____	_____

 FOCUS

Children use a train of Snap Cubes to estimate and measure lengths of objects. Then they record their measurements and choose another object.

HOME CONNECTION

Play a game of 10 questions. Ask: "I am thinking of something in the bedroom that is about two straws long. What is it?" After identifying the object, measure it using a straw. Take turns guessing.

Unit 8, Lesson 2: Estimating Lengths

_____   Date: _____

Ordering Lengths

Put the ropes in order.

[blank framed box]

I put the ropes in order from _____

to _____.

Think of another way to order the ropes.

FOCUS

Children cut out lengths of rope from *Line Master 7: Ordering Lengths,* put them in order according to length, and paste them onto this page.

HOME CONNECTION

Collect various small objects and put them in a pile. Ask your child to order them by length. Ask: "How did you decide the order of the objects?"

188   Unit 8, Lesson 3: Ordering Lengths

Copyright © 2004 Pearson Education Canada Inc. Not to be copied.

Name: _____ Date: _____

Use Different Units

I measured _____.

Unit	Is it longer than 10?	Estimate	Measure
	yes no	about _____	_____
	yes no	about _____	_____
	yes no	about _____	_____
	yes no	about _____	_____

 FOCUS

Children measure the length of an object by choosing different non-standard units.

HOME CONNECTION

Have your child use a piece of string to measure items in your home. Have your child estimate, then count, how many lengths of string fit along the object.

Unit 8, Lesson 4: Choosing a Unit

Choose a Unit

How would you measure your hand and your foot?
Which unit is better? Circle your answer.

Which unit would you use to measure the height of your teacher?
Use pictures, numbers, or words to explain why.

Who Went the Farthest?

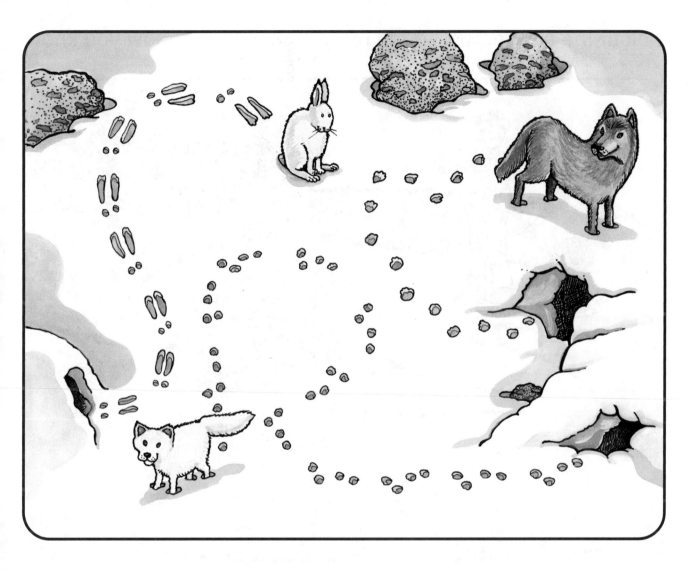

The _____ went the farthest distance.

The _____ went the shortest distance.

 FOCUS

Children compare distances to determine the animal that went the farthest.

HOME CONNECTION

Cut a short length of string. With your child, find three things that are curvy. Use the string to measure which is the longest and which is the shortest.

Name: _____ Date: _____

Which Way Is Shorter?

Colour the shorter way to the ramp. Tell a partner how you know.

 FOCUS

Children identify the shorter route.

 HOME CONNECTION

With your child, print your first names. Ask: "Which name is longer?" You can play this game with other names you know.

Name: _____ Date: _____

About How Many?

About how many cards does it take to cover each object?

Object	Estimate	Measure
	about _____	_____
(My Object)	about _____	_____
(My Object)	about _____	_____

Name: _____ Date: _____

Cover This Shape

Cover this area with Pattern Blocks.
Use only one kind of block each time.

Kind of Block	How Many?
▲	
⬢	
◆	

 FOCUS
Children record the number of each type of Pattern Block required to cover the outline of a hexagon.

 HOME CONNECTION
Ask your child to estimate how many sheets of newspaper it will take to cover a table, a bed, or a carpet. After each estimate, have your child cover the area to determine the actual measure.

Name: _____ Date: _____

Cover the Page

About how many will cover this page?

Object	Estimate	Measure
	about _____	_____
	about _____	_____
	about _____	_____
My Object		
	about _____	_____

 FOCUS
Children estimate the number of each object required to cover this page. Then they record their estimates, cover the page, and record their measurements.

 HOME CONNECTION
With your child, cut out identical paper squares. After estimating how many will cover a larger square, your child covers the surface with the small squares. Together, count the squares.

Unit 8, Lesson 6: Estimating and Comparing Areas **195**

Choose a Unit

About how many units does it take to cover each object?

Object	Estimate	Measure
	about _____	_____
My Object	about _____	_____
My Object	about _____	_____

FOCUS

Children choose a unit and estimate the number they think it will take to cover each object. They record both their estimates and actual measurements.

HOME CONNECTION

Ask your child to estimate how many pasta pieces it would take to cover the surface of a small envelope. Record the estimate and then, with your child, cover the envelope with the objects, count, and compare.

Roll and Cover

Take turns with a partner.

Roll a number cube to see how many blocks you may use.

Work together to cover the rectangle.

How many blocks did you need altogether?

Try it again.

 FOCUS

Children work with small blocks, taking turns to roll a number cube to see how many units they may take to cover the area.

 HOME CONNECTION

Play with your child, using pennies and a number cube.

Unit 8, Lesson 6: Estimating and Comparing Areas

Ordering My Objects

Pick 4 objects.

Trace the objects from shortest to longest.

FOCUS

Children choose objects and put them in order from shortest to longest. They record their results by tracing the objects onto the page.

HOME CONNECTION

Collect at least eight objects in your home and put them on a table. Ask your child to sort them from shortest to longest. Ask: "How did you decide where each object belongs?"

Choose, Estimate, and Measure

Object	Circle the Unit	Estimate	Measure
		about _____	_____
		about _____	_____
		about _____	_____
		about _____	_____

FOCUS

Children find four objects. They choose a unit of measure, use it to estimate, and then record the length of each object.

HOME CONNECTION

Discuss this page with your child. Have your child describe the activity.

Name: _____   Date: _____

My Journal

Tell what you learned about measuring lengths and area.
Use pictures, numbers, or words.

FOCUS

Children reflect on and record what they learned
about linear measurement and area.

HOME CONNECTION

Ask your child to describe what he or she liked best
about measuring lengths and area.

UNIT
9

2-D Geometry and Applications

FOCUS

Children look at a simple line drawing for ten seconds and make a mental picture of it. Then they draw what they remember.

HOME CONNECTION

Invite your child to tell you how he or she remembered this picture when asked to draw it in class.

Name: _____   Date: _____

Dear Family,

Your child will be learning more about 2-D figures—circles, triangles, squares, and rectangles. Your child will learn about applications of math concepts.

The Learning Goals for this unit are to

- Compare and sort 2-D figures according to attributes, such as number of sides or whether they have curves.
- Recognize figures that have symmetry—matching parts.
- Identify "half" or "fair shares" of various objects.
- Tell time to the half-hour.

You can help your child reach these goals by doing the activities suggested at the bottom of each page.

Figure Detectives

What figures do you see?

Circle how many figures you see.

     0   1   2   3   4

     0   1   2   3   4

     0   1   2   3   4

     0   1   2   3   4

 FOCUS
Children find and count the number of 2-D figures they see.

 HOME CONNECTION
Ask your child to show you each figure he or she saw.

Unit 9, Launch: 2-D Geometry and Applications   **203**

Name: _____ Date: _____

Figures That Are Alike

How are these figures alike?	Draw another figure that is like the others.

The figures are alike because_____

_____.

How are these figures alike?	Draw another figure that is like the others.

The figures are alike because _____

_____.

 FOCUS

Children describe how figures in a set are alike. They draw another figure and explain which attributes are shared.

 HOME CONNECTION

Ask your child to tell you how these groups of figures are alike. Together, "hunt" through your home for figures with matching attributes.

Name: _____ Date: _____

My Rectangles

Draw two different [____] .

How are the [____] alike?

_____

_____

How are the [____] different?

_____

_____

FOCUS

Children draw two different rectangles and tell two things about them. Children describe how the rectangles are alike and different.

HOME CONNECTION

Invite your child to draw the faces of two favourite rectangular objects from your home and bring the drawings to school for sharing.

Unit 9, Lesson I: Identify Attributes of 2-D Figures   **205**

My Figure

Tell about your figure.

```
┌──────────────────────────────────────────────┐
│                                                │
│                                                │
│                                                │
│                                                │
│                                                │
│                                                │
│                                                │
│                                                │
│                                                │
│                                                │
│                                                │
│                                                │
└──────────────────────────────────────────────┘
```

Compare with a friend's figure.

How are your figures alike?

Both have _____.

How are they different?

One has _____. One does not.

FOCUS

Children select one figure and tell about it. They compare figures with a partner and note similarities and differences.

HOME CONNECTION

Invite your child to tell about the figure described above. Ask: "What does it remind you of? How would you describe it to someone who cannot see it?"

Name: _____ Date: _____

Sorting 2-D Figures

Circle the figures that are alike.	Paste a figure that is alike.
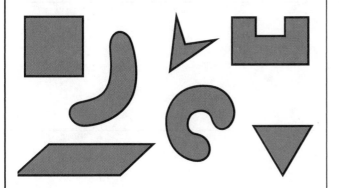	

It is alike because it has _____.

Circle the figures that are alike.	Paste a figure that is alike.

It is alike because it has _____.

 FOCUS

Children circle like figures in the first box, then cut and paste another like figure from *Line Master II: All Kinds of Figures* in the second box. They explain their thinking.

 HOME CONNECTION

Invite your child to find a figure at home that is like the figures circled in each row.

Which Figures Are Alike?

Object	My Matching Figure

FOCUS

Children draw matching figures for each illustration.

HOME CONNECTION

Choose a geometric attribute of a favourite toy—corners, straight sides, curves, dents—and ask your child to find other objects with the same attribute.

What Is the Rule?

These figures are put in a group.

These figures do not belong in the group.

Which of these figures belong in the group? Circle them.

 FOCUS

Children determine what attribute the top figures have in common, check that none of the middle figures has it, then circle the bottom ones that share the same attribute.

 HOME CONNECTION

Invite your child to tell you what this problem is and how he or she solved it.

Name: _____ Date: _____

Find the Rule

These figures are put in a group.

These figures do not belong in the group.

Which of these figures belong in the group? Circle them.

 FOCUS

Children determine what attribute the top figures
have in common, check that none of the middle
figures has it, then circle the bottom ones that share
the same attribute.

 HOME CONNECTION

Invite your child to tell you what this problem is and
how he or she solved it.

Match Figures

Cut and paste the matching figures on top.

FOCUS

Children cut and paste figures from *Line Master 13:*
What Do These Match? to match each figure above.

HOME CONNECTION

Invite your child to look through old magazines, cut
out pictures of square or rectangular things, and
create a picture with the pieces.

Name: _____ Date: _____

Compare Figures

Find all the △ ▢ ◯ ▭ .

This matches.	This is bigger.	This is smaller.
△		
▢		
◯		
▭		

FOCUS

Children cut and paste from *Line Master 14: Compare Figures* to find matching figures and compare the sizes of similar figures.

HOME CONNECTION

Fold a square in half to create a rectangle. Then fold the corners to create triangles. Cut your paper into the folded figures and have your child reassemble them into the original square.

Name: _____ Date: _____

Which Have Matching Parts?

Circle the figures that have matching parts.

Draw Matching Parts

Draw the matching parts to finish the pictures.

FOCUS

Children create a "mirror image" on the right side of each grid. Ensure they begin at the line of symmetry and copy the figures on the opposite side.

HOME CONNECTION

With your child, look for objects in your home or neighbourhood that have "matching parts" (fern leaf, butterfly, dandelion, pine cone, a face).

Name: _____   Date: _____

Show One-Half

Colour one-half of each figure.

 HOME CONNECTION

Help your child cut a sandwich or apple in half to make fair shares. Ask: "How do you know you made fair shares? How can we check?"

Show Fair Shares

Draw a line to show fair shares.

How can you tell these are fair shares?

_____

_____.

 FOCUS

Children draw a line in each picture to show fair
shares or halves, then explain how they know they
have fair shares.

HOME CONNECTION

Your child is practising making fair shares. When
you divide food into servings, ask: "Are they fair
shares? How do you know?"

Name: _____   Date: _____

Time to the Half-Hour

Write each time.

_____

_____

_____

_____

_____

_____

Show the time.

2:30

5:30

11:30

 FOCUS

Children write the times the clocks show or draw hands to show the times indicated.

 HOME CONNECTION

Use a clock with a face to play a game. Set the clock to the half-hour and say: "What time is it Mr. Clock?" Ask your child to tell the time.

Name: _____   Date: _____

What Time Is It?

Show a time on each clock.
Draw a picture to show what you do at each time.

It is _____ in the morning.

It is _____ in the afternoon.

What do you do at 7:30 in the morning that is different from what you do at 7:30 at night?

_____

_____

 FOCUS

Children add hands to the clocks to indicate times to the half-hour and draw pictures to show what they do at those times.

 HOME CONNECTION

Together, draw pictures or make a record to show what your child is doing each half-hour, after school. Look at the clock together, and talk about the position of the hour hand.

All about My Figure

Tell all about your figure.

Use pictures, numbers, or words.

 FOCUS

Children pick a figure, then draw and write to tell everything they can about it.

 HOME CONNECTION

In this activity, your child shows what he or she has learned about figures. Have your child tell you about the figure he or she chose.

Name: _____   Date: _____

I Can Sort Figures

Show a way to sort figures.

All these have _____.

All these do not.

Show another way to sort the figures.

FOCUS

Children sort figures according to an attribute, glue the sorted figures, and write their sorting rule.

HOME CONNECTION

Your child sorted these figures according to a common attribute. Ask him or her to tell you about the sorting rule.

Half of Our Design

Paste your half of the design on this page.

Name some of the figures you used. _____

_____

Tell something special about your design. _____

_____

FOCUS

Children paste half of the "copycat design" they made with a partner. They identify some of its figures and tell about it.

HOME CONNECTION

Invite your child to tell you about this design. Ask: "Why is it called a 'copycat design'?"

Name: _____ Date: _____

My Journal

Tell what you learned about figures.
Use pictures, numbers, or words to show your thinking.

FOCUS

Children reflect on what they learned about figures, fractions, and time to the half-hour in this unit.

HOME CONNECTION

Point to a clock with a face and ask: "What figure is this clock?" When the big hand moves to the 6 and divides the clock in half, we say it is _____. (half-past the hour)

222 Unit 9, Lesson 8: Show What You Know

Copyright © 2004 PEARSON Education Canada Inc. Not to be copied.

Place Value and Number Applications

FOCUS

Children estimate and count the number of children in the picture.

HOME CONNECTION

Look at this picture with your child. Ask your child to estimate the number of children, then count the children together.

Name: _____   Date: _____

Dear Family,

In this unit, your child will be exploring some important mathematical concepts—estimating, grouping by 10's, and place value.

The Learning Goals for this unit are to

- Compare and order numbers using materials and drawings.
- Estimate and count large collections of objects (up to 100).
- Use a calculator to explore numbers and check answers.
- Solve number problems and word problems and explain their strategies.

You can help your child reach these goals by doing the activities suggested at the bottom of each page.

Name: _____ Date: _____

How Many Beetles?

About how many beetles are there?

Circle your answer.

more than 50   about 50   less than 50

My estimate is _____.

I counted _____.

 FOCUS

Children estimate the number of beetles that are on the page and then count them.

 HOME CONNECTION

Fill a jar with up to 50 small household objects such as pennies, bread tags, or macaroni. Say: "About how many are in the jar? Now count to see how close you are."

What Is Missing?

Write the missing numbers on the chart.

1	2	3	4	5	6	7	8	9	10
11	12	13	14	15	16	17	18	19	20
21	22	23	24			27	28	29	30
31	32	33	34	35	36		38	39	40
41	42	43	44	45			48	49	50
51	52	53	54	55		57	58		
61	62	63	64	65		67	68	69	70
		73	74	75	76	77	78	79	80
81		83	84	85	86	87		89	90
91	92		94	95	96	97		99	100

FOCUS

Children fill in the missing numbers on a 100-chart.

HOME CONNECTION

Your child is learning about numbers to 100. Show one of the page numbers between 50 and 100 from a book or magazine. Ask: "What is the next page number? What was the last one? How do you know?"

Find Two Patterns

Find a pattern. Circle the numbers.

What is your pattern? _____

Find another pattern. Colour the numbers.

What is your pattern? _____

1	2	3	4	5	6	7	8	9	10
11	12	13	14	15	16	17	18	19	20
21	22	23	24	25	26	27	28	29	30
31	32	33	34	35	36	37	38	39	40
41	42	43	44	45	46	47	48	49	50
51	52	53	54	55	56	57	58	59	60
61	62	63	64	65	66	67	68	69	70
71	72	73	74	75	76	77	78	79	80
81	82	83	84	85	86	87	88	89	90
91	92	93	94	95	96	97	98	99	100

 FOCUS

Children find and mark patterns on a 100-chart.

 HOME CONNECTION

Your child is learning about patterns in numbers. Use this chart to practise counting by 1's, 2's, 5's, and 10's to 100.

Name: _____ Date: _____

Counting Two Ways

Make groups of 10's. Draw a picture.

```
_____ 10's        _____ left over        _____ in all
```

Count another way.

Show how you counted. Use pictures, numbers, or words.

```
_____ in all
```

FOCUS
Children count a collection of objects in two different ways.

HOME CONNECTION
Ask your child to show you two different ways of counting the number of fingers of all the members of your family (by 5's or 10's).

Counting Nails

Circle groups of 10's. Use a blue crayon.

Circle groups in another way. Use a red crayon.

 FOCUS

Using two different colours of crayons, children draw circles around groups of nails to show two different ways to count them.

 HOME CONNECTION

Your child is learning to count groups of objects in different ways. Ask your child to show you two different ways to count the number of eyes of all the members of your family (count by 1's or 2's).

Bee Count

How many bees are there?
Show how you counted.

[ ]

Count the bees another way.
Show how you counted.

[ ]

FOCUS

Children count the bees in two ways.

HOME CONNECTION

Pose a problem to your child, such as: "How many knives, forks, and spoons are in the drawer? Think of two different ways to count them."

Spill the Beans

Spill the beans.

Estimate the number. _____

Make groups of 10's to show how you counted.

```
┌─────────────────────────────────────────────────────────────┐
│                                                             │
│                                                             │
│                                                             │
│                                                             │
│                                                             │
│                                                             │
│                                                             │
└─────────────────────────────────────────────────────────────┘
```

Spill the counters.

Estimate the number. _____

Make groups of 10's to show how you counted.

```
┌─────────────────────────────────────────────────────────────┐
│                                                             │
│                                                             │
│                                                             │
│                                                             │
│                                                             │
│                                                             │
└─────────────────────────────────────────────────────────────┘
```

 FOCUS

Children estimate the number of objects in two different collections, make and record groups of 10's, and the number left over in each collection.

 HOME CONNECTION

Fill a bag with small objects. Show your child a group of 10 of the objects. Ask your child to use the group of 10 to estimate the number in the bag, then count the objects by grouping in 10's.

Estimating Counters

Take a scoop of counters.

Estimate the number. _____

Place the counters in the ten-frames.

<table>
<tr><td></td><td></td><td></td><td></td><td></td></tr>
<tr><td></td><td></td><td></td><td></td><td></td></tr>
</table>

<table>
<tr><td></td><td></td><td></td><td></td><td></td></tr>
<tr><td></td><td></td><td></td><td></td><td></td></tr>
</table>

<table>
<tr><td></td><td></td><td></td><td></td><td></td></tr>
<tr><td></td><td></td><td></td><td></td><td></td></tr>
</table>

<table>
<tr><td></td><td></td><td></td><td></td><td></td></tr>
<tr><td></td><td></td><td></td><td></td><td></td></tr>
</table>

How many groups of 10's? _____

How many left over? _____

How many in all? _____

FOCUS

Children scoop a cup of counters and estimate how many there are. They place the counters on the ten-frames to find an accurate count. They colour the ten-frames to record their work.

HOME CONNECTION

Place 30 to 50 small countable objects (macaroni, beans, paper clips) in a plastic bag. Ask: "How many objects are in the bag?" Have your child count the objects by placing them in groups of 10's.

Name: _____ Date: _____

Groups of 10's

Take 2 handfuls of Snap Cubes.

Estimate the number. _____
Make trains of 10's.
Show your trains. Use pictures, numbers, or words.

How many trains of 10's? _____

How many left over? _____

How many Snap Cubes are there in all?

_____ 10's   _____ left over   _____ in all

 FOCUS

Children take handfuls of Snap Cubes and make trains of 10's. They record how many 10's, how many 1's, and how many Snap Cubes there are in all.

 HOME CONNECTION

Save egg cartons and cut off two sections so there are 10 sections in each carton. Collect small objects and use the egg cartons to practise counting (e.g., 3 cartons full and 2 left over: 10, 20, 30, 31, 32.)

Name: _____ Date: _____

Show Your Number

Count your objects.

How many do you have? _____

Draw a picture to show how many.

Groups of 10's	1's (leftovers)

How many 10's? _____   How many 1's? _____

Print the numeral.

10's	1's

28 Beans

Draw 28 beans.

Circle groups of 10's.

There are _____ groups of 10's and _____ 1's.

Print the numeral.

10's	1's

FOCUS

Children draw 28 beans and circle groups of 10's.
They record the number of beans as a numeral.

HOME CONNECTION

Select a number between 20 and 30. Ask your child
to draw that number of circles or squares. Help your
child circle the groups of 10's; then make a 10's and
1's chart like the one on this page.

Name: _____ Date: _____

Butterflies Everywhere

How many butterflies? _____

How many 10's? _____ How many 1's? _____
Print the numeral.

10's	1's

 FOCUS

Children count the butterflies by 1's and then circle
groups of 10's. This page provides reinforcement of
the use of 0 as a placeholder.

 HOME CONNECTION

Provide 50 small objects (e.g., coins, buttons.) Count
them by 1's; then group by 10's, and write the numeral
50. Ask: "When we write 50, what does the 5 mean?"
(5 tens) "What does the zero mean?" (0 ones)

Numbers Race!

Work with a partner.
Take turns. Find each missing number.

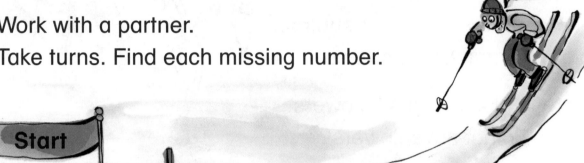

Start

$12 - 9 =$ _____

_____ $+ 4 = 10$ $4 +$ _____ $= 9$

$16 - 10 =$ _____

$8 +$ _____ $= 14$

_____ $+ 7 = 11$ $15 -$ _____ $= 9$

$15 +$ _____ $= 17$

$18 - 17 =$ _____

$13 - 8 =$ _____

_____ $+ 9 = 14$

$11 - 7 =$ _____

Finish

 FOCUS

Children work together to complete addition and
subtraction sentences.

 HOME CONNECTION

Make up simple number stories for your child to
solve. (For example, There are 8 shoes by the door,
and 4 boots. How many shoes and boots are there
altogether?)

Name: _____ Date: _____

More Problems to Solve

Circle **+** or **−** to add or subtract.
Complete the number sentence.

There are 16 plants. 8 have flowers.
How many do not have flowers?

+   **−**

_____ ◯ _____ = _____

6 pink roses are in a vase. 6 red roses are added.
How many are there altogether?

+   **−**

_____ ◯ _____ = _____

14 leaves are on a branch. 5 fall off.
How many leaves are still on the branch?

+   **−**

_____ ◯ _____ = _____

There are 18 black ants. 10 red ants came along.
How many more black ants than red ants are there?

+   **−**

_____ ◯ _____ = _____

FOCUS
Children decide which operation to use to solve a
word problem, then solve the problem.

HOME CONNECTION
Review the problems on this page with your child.
Together, make up similar problems and talk about
whether to add or subtract to solve them.

Count On, Count Back

5	9	11	2	3
+ 3	+ 2	+ 1	+ 14	+ 12
_____	_____	_____	_____	_____

$0 + 11 =$ _____ $3 + 8 =$ _____ $2 + 15 =$ _____

Count back to subtract.

10	12	14	15	11
− 3	− 2	− 3	− 1	− 2
_____	_____	_____	_____	_____

$16 − 1 =$ _____ $13 − 2 =$ _____ $17 − 3 =$ _____

Write a number sentence.

12
3 fly away.

15
3 more come.

 = _____   _____ ◯ _____ = _____

FOCUS

Children use counting on and counting back to complete addition and subtraction sentences.

HOME CONNECTION

Have your child tell about one of the number sentences recorded on the page. Ask your child: "How did counting on or counting back help you find number sentences?"

Adding with Doubles

Find the sums. Use doubles to help.

5 + 5 = _____   9 + 9 = _____   3 + 3 = _____

```
    7              6           4            8
  + 7            + 6         + 4          + 8
  ____           ____        ____         ____
```

Find the sums. Circle the doubles.

```
    2              5           4            1
  + 2            + 7         + 6          + 1
  ____           ____        ____         ____
```

```
    4              9           3            8
  + 9            + 9         + 6          + 9
  ____           ____        ____         ____
```

FOCUS

Children use counters to make, record, and identify doubles facts.

HOME CONNECTION

Ask your child to tell a number story about one of the doubles facts.

All about Wheels

There are 4 objects in the yard.
Altogether, there are 12 wheels in the yard.
Which objects are in the yard?

Use pictures, numbers, or words to solve the problem.

Name: _____ Date: _____

Rolling Along

Five toys are in the toy box.

Altogether, there are 13 wheels in the toy box.

Which toys are in the toy box?

Use pictures, numbers, or words to solve the problem.

 FOCUS

Children solve a problem using pictures, numbers, or words.

HOME CONNECTION

Ask your child to explain the solution to the problem.

The Answer Is 20

The display on the calculator reads 20.

How many ways can you find to make 20 appear in the display?

 FOCUS

Children use a calculator to find as many number sentences for 20 as they can.

 HOME CONNECTION

Choose a number between 10 and 30. Have your child use a calculator to find number sentences that result in that number (for example, for 25: 20 + 5; 19 + 6; 26 − 1; 27 − 2…).

Name: _____ Date: _____

Choose Your Own Answer!

And the answer is _____!

Use your calculator.

Find as many ways as you can to get your answer.

FOCUS

Children use calculators to find as many ways as
they can to get the target number they select.
They can both add and subtract and use more than
2 numbers.

HOME CONNECTION

The next time you go grocery shopping with your
child, take a calculator. Ask your child to use the
calculator to add the number of items in your grocery
cart.

244   **Unit 10, Lesson 6:** Strategies Tool Kit

Copyright © 2004 Pearson Education Canada Inc. Not to be copied.

Be a Number Detective!

Read the clues. Find the numbers.
Then make up your own detective story.
Trade with a friend and solve.

The number has a 6 and a 4 in it. It is a number more than 50.

The number is _____.

The number is less than 50 and more than 45 and has a 6 in it.

The number is _____.

The number is between 50 and 80 and has two 6's.

The number is _____.

The number _____

_____.

The number is _____.

 FOCUS

Children read clues to solve number problems.
Then, they create their own number detective story
and exchange it with a partner to solve.

HOME CONNECTION

Ask your child to explain how he or she solved the
problems on this page.

Name: _____ Date: _____

What's the Number?

Read the clues. Find the numbers.

The number has a 3 and a 2 in it.
The number is more than 30.

The number is _____.

The number is less than 60 and more than 57 and has a 9 in it.

The number is _____.

The number is between 40 and 70 and has two 5's.

The number is _____.

Make Your Own

FOCUS

Children read the clues to solve number problems.
In the last box, they create their own number story
and exchange it with a partner to solve.

HOME CONNECTION

Cut a long paper strip and write numbers in
sequence (for example, from 15 to 30). Cover a
number with a finger, and have your child tell you the
number. Take turns covering numbers and guessing.

The Dancers!

Make an addition story about the picture.

Write the number sentence. _____

Make a subtraction story about the picture.

Write the number sentence. _____

 FOCUS

Children create and record addition and subtraction
stories about the picture.

 HOME CONNECTION

Ask your child to explain how he or she thought of
the number story. Look at the picture together and
make and solve more number stories.

Name: _____ Date: _____

How Many Buttons?

Look at the button blanket.

About how many buttons are there? _____

Circle groups of 10's. Use an orange crayon.

How many groups of 10's? _____

How many are left over? _____

How many in all? _____

Circle groups in another way. Use a green crayon.
Show how you counted, using pictures, numbers, or words.

 FOCUS

Children count the buttons on a button blanket using 10's and 1's, and in another way.

HOME CONNECTION

Ask your child to explain how he or she solved the problem. Ask: "How did you make sure you didn't count any buttons twice?"

My Button Blanket

How many 10's did you use? _____

How many extra 1's? _____

How many buttons in all? _____

 FOCUS

Children design a button blanket. They estimate and
record the number of buttons used.

 HOME CONNECTION

Ask your child to explain how he or she solved the
problem. Ask: "How did you make sure you didn't
count any buttons twice?"

Name: _____ Date: _____

My Journal

When can you estimate?

How can you group by 10's to help you estimate and count?

Use pictures, numbers, or words to show your thinking.

 FOCUS

Children reflect on and record what they learned about estimation in this unit.

 HOME CONNECTION

Ask your child, "What did you learn about how to estimate? How can you group by 10's to help you estimate?"

Unit 10, Lesson 7: Show What You Know

Mass and Capacity

Name: _____   Date: _____

Dear Family,

In this unit, your child will develop an understanding of *mass*, the relative heaviness of an object, and *capacity*, how much a container can hold.

The Learning Goals for this unit are to

- Compare the capacity of containers by filling them with water and other materials.
- Estimate how much a container will hold and which of two containers will hold more.
- Compare and estimate the mass of objects using simple scales and balances.
- Solve everyday problems about mass and capacity.

You can help your child reach these goals by doing the activities suggested at the bottom of each page.

I Can Compare

Circle the word that compares the pictures.

 is (**taller**   **shorter**) than .

 is (**longer**   **shorter**) than .

 is (**colder**   **hotter**) than .

 is (**wider**   **taller**) than   .

FOCUS

Using comparison terms, children apply concepts learned in Unit 8 to compare two objects.

HOME CONNECTION

Have your child compare different objects in your home.

Unit II, Launch: Mass and Capacity   **253**

Name: _____ Date: _____

More or Less Water?

Which holds more water?
Circle the one that holds more.

 FOCUS

Children compare two objects and decide which
holds more.

 HOME CONNECTION

Have your child compare which of two plastic
containers holds more. At a sink, have your child fill
one container with water, and then pour that water
into another container to see if it overflows.

About the Same

Look at the first picture in each row.
Colour the picture that holds about the same.

FOCUS

Children identify which container holds about the same as the first container pictured in the row.

HOME CONNECTION

At a sink, have your child experiment by pouring water from one plastic container to another to find two containers that hold about the same amount of water.

Name: _____ Date: _____

Estimate Scoops

About how many scoops does each container hold?
Use a scoop to estimate and measure.

Container	Estimates			Measure
	Estimate	After 2 Scoops	After 5 Scoops	
1				
2				
3				

What did you find out about estimating?
Tell about your thinking. Use pictures, numbers, or words.

FOCUS

Children estimate and measure the capacities of different containers.

HOME CONNECTION

Experiment with your child using water or rice and two different-sized containers. Ask your child to estimate the number of times the contents from the smaller container can be poured into the larger one.

How Many Will Fill It?

Container	Estimate
There are 5 shovels of sand in this bag.	It holds about _____ shovels.
There are 3 boxes in this bin.	It holds about _____ boxes.
There are 4 spoonfuls of water in this glass.	It holds about _____ spoonfuls.

Write your own.

There are _____ scoops in this jar.	It holds about _____ scoops.

 FOCUS

Children use what they know about a smaller container to estimate how much a larger container will hold.

 HOME CONNECTION

Provide dry ingredients such as rice and two different-sized containers. Ask your child to estimate how many times the rice from the smaller container can be poured into the larger one.

Name: _____ Date: _____

How Many Scoops?

Two scoops fill a pail.

How many scoops will fill 6 pails?

Show your thinking in pictures, numbers, or words.

 FOCUS

Children choose a strategy to solve the problem.

 HOME CONNECTION

Have your child explain the solution to the problem. Ask: "How did you know the number of scoops needed to fill 6 pails?"

Name: _____ Date: _____

How Many Pails?

I5 scoops fill 3 pails.

How many pails will hold 25 scoops?

Show your thinking in pictures, numbers, or words.

Name: _____ Date: _____

Compare Mass

Draw 2 objects that have about the same mass as the stapler.

Draw 2 objects that are lighter than the stapler.

Draw 2 objects that are heavier than the stapler.

 FOCUS

Children compare the mass of a stapler to other objects found in the classroom.

 HOME CONNECTION

Choose an object with your child and compare its heaviness to that of other objects in your home.

Name: _____ Date: _____

Heavier or Lighter?

Which object is heavier? Which object is lighter?
Use real objects to find out.

The pencil is _____
than the book.

The stapler is _____
than the Pattern Block.

The paper clip is _____
than the Snap Cube.

The chalk brush is _____
than the marker.

FOCUS

Children compare some common objects to
determine which is heavier or lighter.

HOME CONNECTION

Collect several household objects. Have your child
practise holding one in each hand to determine
which is heavier or lighter.

Name: _____   Date: _____

Lighter, about the Same, or Heavier?

Look at each picture.
Is the object **lighter than, about the same as,**
or **heavier than** your notebook?
Circle your answer.

lighter   about the same   heavier

lighter   about the same   heavier

lighter   about the same   heavier

lighter   about the same   heavier

lighter   about the same   heavier

lighter   about the same   heavier

 FOCUS

Children compare the relative heaviness of some common objects to their notebooks.

 HOME CONNECTION

Make a balance by attaching a plastic bag to each end of a coat hanger. Put an object into each bag. Balance the hanger on your finger. The heavier object will pull the hanger down on that side.

Name: _____ Date: _____

Heavier or Lighter Than 5?

Use 5 Snap Cubes. Choose 4 objects.
Are the objects heavier or lighter than 5 Snap Cubes?

Estimate. Use a balance scale to check.

Object	Heavier Than 5?	
	Estimate	Measure

What did you find out about estimating?
Tell about your thinking. Use pictures, numbers, or words.

FOCUS

Children estimate and measure the masses of different objects, using a non-standard unit.

HOME CONNECTION

Play guessing games where you take turns creating your own "What object is about as heavy as 15 _____?" Be sure to identify the non-standard unit (for example, grapes, pennies), before solving the problem.

Copyright © 2004 Pearson Education Canada Inc. Not to be copied.   Unit II, Lesson 5: Estimating Mass   **263**

Measuring Popcorn

Circle your choice. Which is heavier?

or

What did you find out? Which is heavier?

or

Estimate! About how many kernels will balance
our container of popped popcorn? Circle your choice.

more than 20   less than 20

What did you find out? _____

_____

Show an object that has about the same mass as 20 kernels.

 FOCUS

Children compare the masses of unpopped and
popped popcorn.

 HOME CONNECTION

Ask your child to explain the problem on this page.

Name: _____ Date: _____

How Much Does It Hold?

or

How would you find out which bag holds more?
Show your thinking in pictures, numbers, or words.

Make a new popcorn problem!

FOCUS
Children show which bag of popcorn holds more,
then create another problem.

HOME CONNECTION
Make popcorn. Before serving it, ask your child to
estimate how many small serving bowls the popcorn
bag or container holds. Work together to fill the
bowls one at a time and check.

Name: _____   Date: _____

My Journal

Tell what you learned about
measuring mass and capacity.
Use pictures, numbers, or words to show your thinking.

FOCUS

Children reflect on and record what they learned
about mass and capacity.

HOME CONNECTION

Ask your child: "What do you like best about
measuring mass and capacity? Why do you think
estimating mass and capacity is important?"

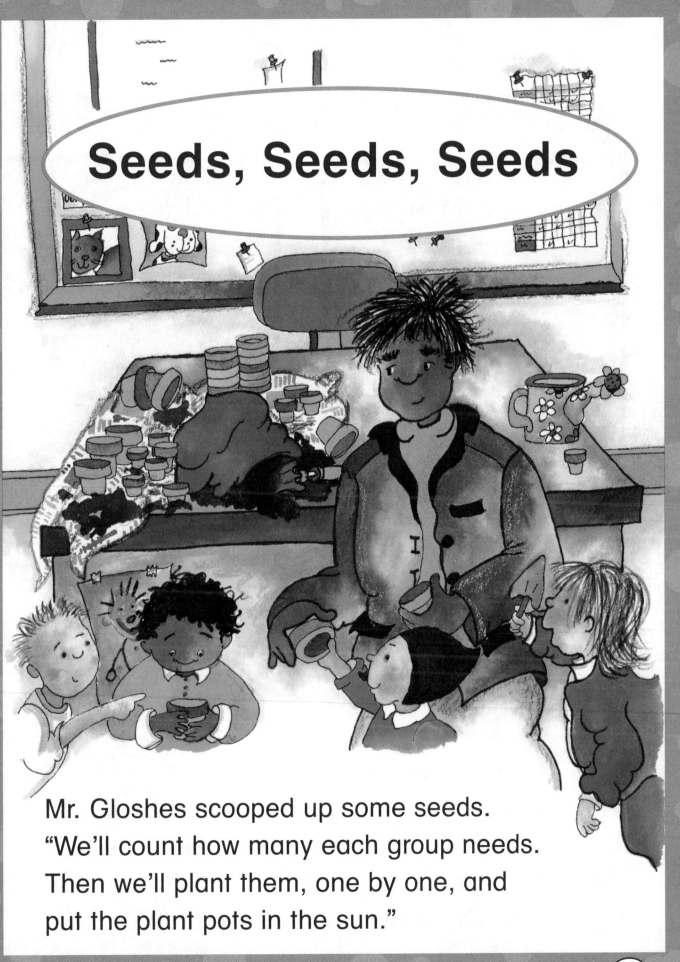

Seeds, Seeds, Seeds

Mr. Gloshes scooped up some seeds.
"We'll count how many each group needs.
Then we'll plant them, one by one, and
put the plant pots in the sun."

They watered the seeds, and watched them too,
But still no plants were breaking through.
On Friday when it was time to go, the class
wondered, "On Monday, will plants show?"

They raced to look when Monday came.
Something in the room was not the same.
All they could do was stop and stare.
The plants were gone! The plants weren't there!

"How will we know if they've started to sprout?
Where did they go?" the class cried out.
Mr.Gloshes scratched his head.
"I think I know," Mr. Gloshes said.

Then someone knocked at the classroom door.
She knocked again, then knocked some more.
The school helper, Mary, was in the hall—
with every plant! She had them all!

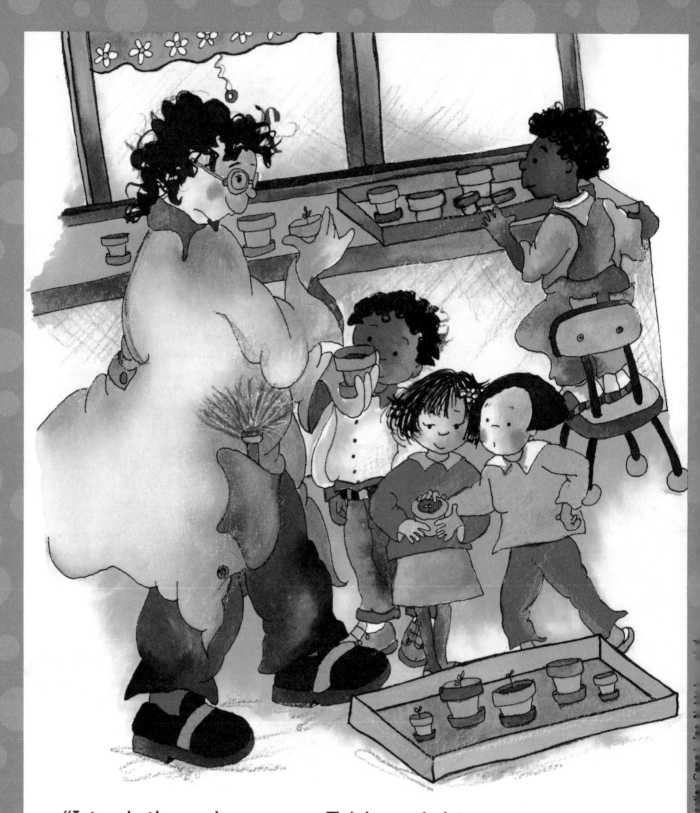

"I took them home on Friday night.
I thought they might get too much light.
I watered them carefully every day.
I'm pretty sure they're all okay."

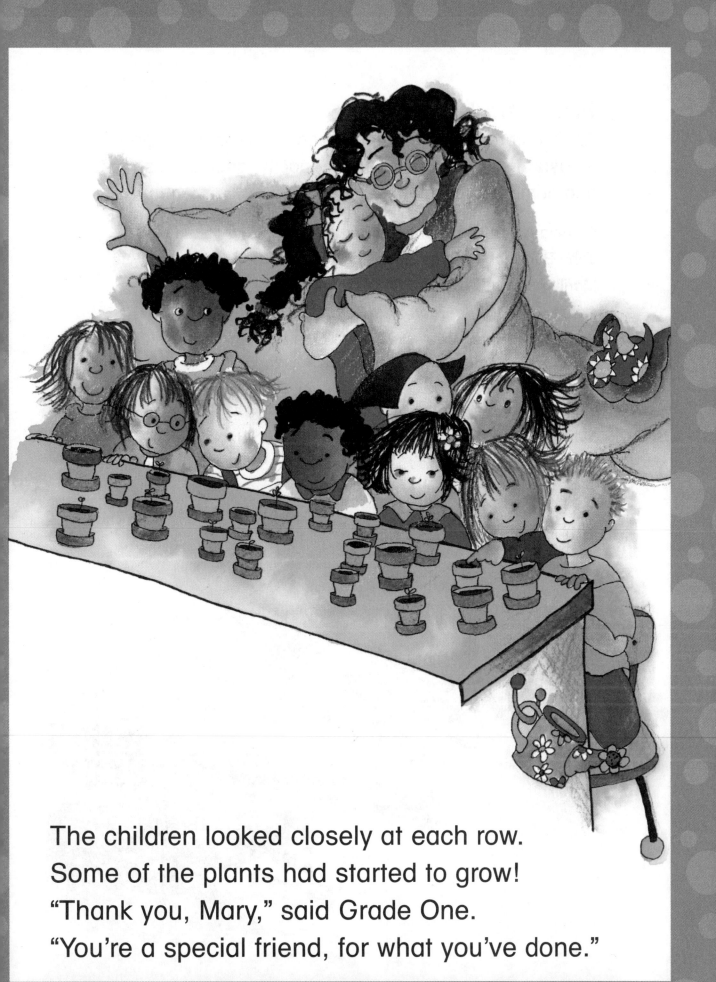

The children looked closely at each row.
Some of the plants had started to grow!
"Thank you, Mary," said Grade One.
"You're a special friend, for what you've done."

From the Library

Ask the librarian about other good books to share about measuring objects, mass and capacity, geometric shapes, and numbers.

Pamela Allen, *Who Sank the Boat?* (Puffin, 1996)

John Burningham, *The Shopping Basket* (Random House, 1992)

Marilyn Burns, *The Greedy Triangle* (Scholastic, 1995)

Aubrey Davis, *The Enormous Potato* (Kids Can Press, 2003)

Susan Hightower, *Twelve Snails to One Lizard: A Tale of Mischief and Measurement* (Simon and Schuster, 1997)

Tana Hoban, *So Many Circles So Many Squares* (Greenwillow, 1998)

Marthe Jocelyn, *Hannah's Collection* (Dutton Books, 2000)

Pam Munoz Ryan, *One Hundred Is a Family* (Hyperion Books, 1996)

Growing Plants

Estimate and Count the Seeds

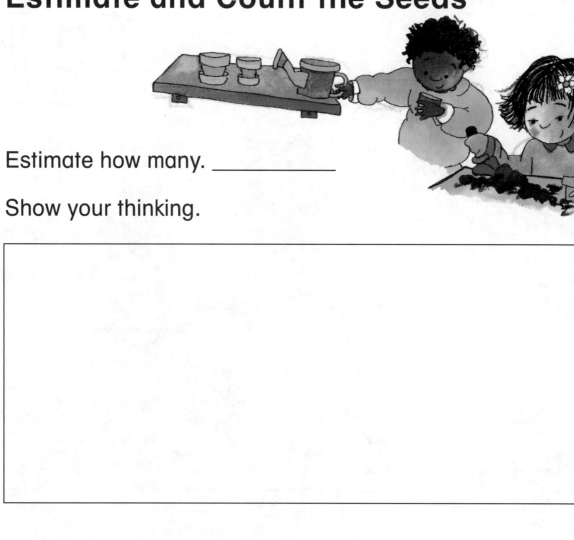

Estimate how many. _____

Show your thinking.

Count how many. _____

Are there *more*, *the same*, or *less* than you estimated?

    more   same   less

How many more? _____

How many less? _____

 Hint Remember to estimate before you count.

276

Share the Seeds

How could you share the seeds with 3 friends?

Use pictures, numbers, or words to show your thinking.

How many seeds would you and each friend have?

_____   _____   _____   _____

 You will need 4 sets of seeds.

Plant the Seeds

What kind of seeds are you planting? _____ seeds

Estimate how many scoops of dirt you will need.

_____ scoops

Find out how many scoops.

_____ scoops

Did you need *more*, *the same*, or *less* than your estimate?

more   same   less

 Record what you found out as you planted your seeds.

278

When Will It Sprout?

Draw your seeds in the box for today.

Make a circle in the box to show when you think your seeds will sprout.

Cross off each day.

Draw the sprout in the box when you first see it!

This week

Sunday	Monday	Tuesday	Wednesday	Thursday	Friday	Saturday

Next week

Sunday	Monday	Tuesday	Wednesday	Thursday	Friday	Saturday

The week after next

Sunday	Monday	Tuesday	Wednesday	Thursday	Friday	Saturday

My seeds took _____ days to sprout.

Hint Remember to check your plant pot every day.

Watch It Grow

Choose a unit.

Estimate and measure how tall your plant is each day.

Record your estimates and measures.

Day	Estimate	Measure
	about _____	about _____
	about _____	about _____
	about _____	about _____
	about _____	about _____
	about _____	about _____
	about _____	about _____
	about _____	about _____
	about _____	about _____

How Much Will It Hold?

Collect lots of different-sized containers from around your home.

Think about how much water each container might hold, and order the containers from the smallest to the largest.

Now add water!
It's time to see if you were right.

What Number Am I?

I have 2 digits.
I am more than a dozen.
I am less than 18.
When you add my 2 digits together, you'll get 5.
What number am I?

It's your turn now.
Make up some number riddles of your own.

Hint! Use the 100-chart on page 7 to help you.

Fold

Math at Home

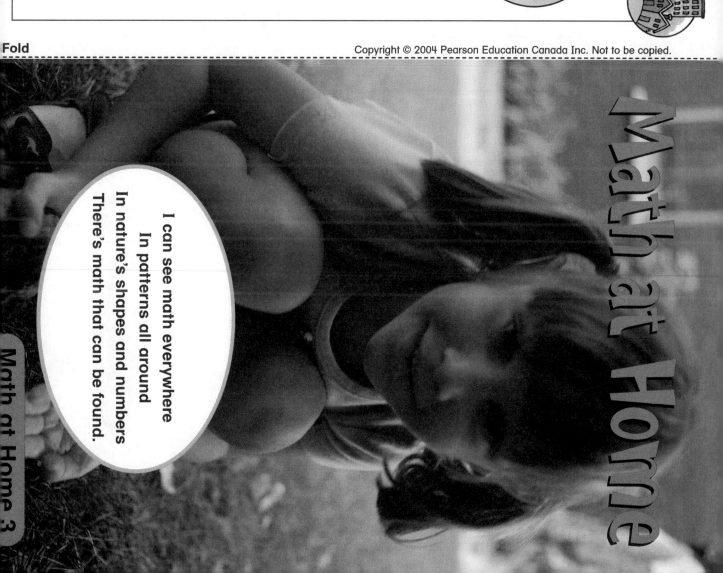

I can see math everywhere
In patterns all around
In nature's shapes and numbers
There's math that can be found.

100-Chart Game Board

1	2	3	4	5	6	7	8	9	10
11	12	13	14	15	16	17	18	19	20
21	22	23	24	25	26	27	28	29	30
31	32	33	34	35	36	37	38	39	40
41	42	43	44	45	46	47	48	49	50
51	52	53	54	55	56	57	58	59	60
61	62	63	64	65	66	67	68	69	70
71	72	73	74	75	76	77	78	79	80
81	82	83	84	85	86	87	88	89	90
91	92	93	94	95	96	97	98	99	100

Shopping for 3-D Solids

On your next visit to the grocery store, look at the different 3-D solids on the shelves.
How many different solids can you find?

Balancing Act

What's wrong with this picture?

Draw items on both sides so this picture makes sense.
What is another way to balance the scale?

Pattern Parade

Game

You'll need:
- 20 counters
- 100-chart game board

On your turn:
- Place 15 to 20 counters on the game board in a pattern.
- Your partner must guess the numbers hidden under each counter.

Take turns until someone gets to 10.

- If your partner guesses them all, score 1 point.
- If your partner notices a pattern, score 1 more point.

Can you think of a different game to play with the same game board?

Under Cover

Game

You'll need:
- 12 small objects (pennies, buttons, bingo chips)
- 2 pieces of paper

On your turn:
- Ask your partner to turn around.
- Place some objects on one piece of paper in an interesting way.

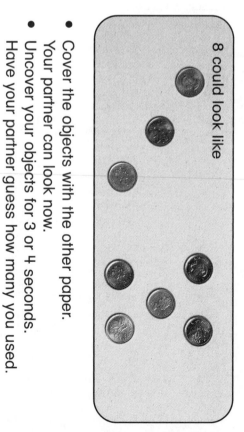

8 could look like

- Cover the objects with the other paper. Your partner can look now.
- Uncover your objects for 3 or 4 seconds. Have your partner guess how many you used.

- If the guess is right, score 2 points.
- If the guess is close, score 1 point.
- Decide together how many points you need to win!

Match the Figures

You'll need:
- 3 cut-outs on heavy paper of each of these figures

Put them in a bag you can't see through.

Time to play:
- Pull one figure from the bag. Name it.
- Can you find a 3-D object where you live that has one surface the same as the figure you are holding?

- If you find an object, keep the cut-out.
- The person who ends up with the most cut-outs is the winner.

Which figure was the hardest to match?

Why do you think so?

Which was easiest?

Fair Is Fair

Game

Divide the pizza into two fair shares. Choose toppings from the list and draw them on your half of the pizza. Let a friend choose toppings for the other half.

Toppings

mushrooms
ham
pineapple
onions

cheese
pepperoni
peppers
olives